Art Center College of Design
Library
1700 Lida Street
Pasadena, Calif. 91103

ART CENTER COLLEGE OF DESIGN

3 3220 00247 2616

741.67090511
J35
2008

映像作家
100人
2008

JAPANESE
MOTION GRAPHIC
CREATORS 2008

Bug News Network

Art Center College Library
1700 Lida St.
Pasadena, CA 91103

Copyright © 2008 by BNN, Inc.

Published by
BNN, Inc.
35 Sankyo Bldg., 3-7-2, Irifune
Chuo-ku, Tokyo 104-0042 Japan
Mail: info@bnn.co.jp

Editors
Yusuke Shouno, Kurando Furuya, Natsumi Fujita

Cooperation
Masahiro Hattori, yoyo., Nagako Hayashi, Koji Yamaguchi

Thanks to
Kana Yamamoto

Cover Designed by
Akinobu Maeda

Illustration(P004-009)
Midori Kawano

Photo(P012-031)
Tomoyuki Morikawa

Translated by
Jeremy Harley, Natsumi Fujita

Managed by
Sayaka Ishii

NOTICE:
All rights reserved. No part of this publication maybe
reproduced, stored in a retrieval system or transmitted
in any form or by any means, electronic, mechanical,
photocopying, recording or otherwise, without
permission of the copyright holder.

ISBN 978-4-86100-576-3

Printed in Japan by SHINANO CO., LTD.

TABLE OF CONTENTS

※本文中の各連絡先・URL アドレスは、2008 年 4 月時点のものであり、予告なしに変更される
　可能性がございます。弊社ではサポート致しかねることをご了承下さい。
※本文中の作品名、プロジェクト名、クライアント名、ブランド名、商品名、その他の固有名詞、
　発表年度に関しては、作家各自より提示された情報をもとに掲載しています。
※本文中の製品名は、各社の商標または登録商標であり、それぞれの帰属者の所有物です。

Art Center College Library
1700 Lida St.
Pasadena, CA 91103

DVD CONTENTS

※付録DVDに収録した映像は、オリジナル作品を短くカットするなど再編集がなされており、いずれも各作家１分程度となっております。

※再生には、DVDビデオ対応の再生機を用いてください。各再生機の操作に関しては、ご使用になる機器の取扱説明書をご参照ください。尚、DVD専用再生機で再生すると、よりきれいな画面でご覧になれます。

※一部の作品に、明滅を繰り返す光を画面演出に用いた映像表現があります。明るい部屋で少し離れた位置からご鑑賞されるよう、ご注意ください。

※有償・無償に拘らず、無断で貸与・複製・公衆送信・上映等を行うことを禁止致します。

01 **阿部伸吾 ABE SHINGO**
Vermillion
(©abeshingo, 2004)
Director + Animation: 阿部伸吾 Shingo Abe

02 **AC部 AC-BU**
AFTER EFFECTS ABC
(©AC-bu, 2007)

03 **アミカ AMICA**
おはなしの花 *Ohanashi no Hana*
(©Amica Kubo + Seita Inoue, 2006)
Director: Amica Kubo + Seita Inoue
Animation : Amica Kubo

04 **アンテナ ANTENNA**
Antenna Works Collection
Movie: Antenna, Music: Metalob

05 **新井風愉 FUYU ARAI**
HAPPY WEDDING
(©Futari, 2007)
Director: 新井風愉 Fuyu Arai
Planning: といだあずさ Toida Azusa, Staring: ふたり Futari

06 **キャドセンター CAD CENTER CORPORATION**
Odilon Redon, *NOIR* DVD&展覧会CM
〈渋谷駅前Q-FRONTスクリーン放映版〉
(©CAD CENTER CORPORATION, 2007)
Director: 大槻一雅 Kazumasa Otsuki
CG Animation: キャドセンタークリエイティブスタジオ CAD CENTER CREATIVE STUDIO
Collection: 岐阜県美術館 THE MUSEUM OF FINE ARTS, GIFU
DVD Pranning + Production + Sales: CAD CENTER CORPORATION

07 **權奇晶 KEE. J. CUON**
STARLEAGUE (ongamenet ON•MEDIA Corp., 2007)
ANIMAX (©Animax Broadcast Japan Inc., 2007)

08 **ドロップ DOLLOP**
COLON (2006)
WOW10 exhibition at TENT LONDON (2007)
Pattern on Wallpaper (2006)

09 **エレクロトニック ELECROTNIK**
NIKE JAPAN+YOKOHAMA F・MARINOS
Director: ELECROTNIK
Advertising Agency: Daiko Advertising Inc.
Production: TAIYO KIKAKU co.,ltd

10 **エンライトメント ENLIGHTENMENT**
What makes you smile ? Enlightenment ver.
(TAICOCLUB, 2008)

11 **ユーフラテス EUPHRATES**
真心ブラザーズ「きみとぼく」
Magokoro Brothers, *Kimi to Boku* (©Ki/oon Records Inc., 2007)
栗コーダーカルテット「おじいさんの11ヶ月」
Kuricorder Quartet, *Grandpapa's Eleven Month*
「栗コーダーカルテット/笛社会」収録
(Licenced by GENEON ENTERTAINMENT INC.)
DNP「イデアの工場」
FACTORY OF IDEAS (©Dai Nippon Printing Co., Ltd., 2006)
ISSEY MIYAKE「A-POC INSIDE.」
(©ISSEY MIYAKE INC., 2007)

12 **後藤章治 SHOJI GOTO**
OOIOO, *UMO*
(©felicity / SHOCKCITY / THRILL JOCKEY, 2006)
Director: 後藤章輔 SHOJI GOTO (EAGLE DESIGN)
Camera : 立川晋輔 Shinsuke Tatsukawa, Editor: 立川晋輔 Shinsuke Tatsukawa,
大嶋明英 Akihide Oshima
Animator (Puppet): 船引亜樹 Aki Funabiki (Pico• Pictures), 富岡淳
Animator (CG) : 大嶋明英 Akihide Oshima, Music: OOIOO

13 **半崎信朗 TOSHIAKI HANZAKI**
Birthday (Toshiaki Hanzaki, 2007)

14 **橋本ダイスケ DAISUKE HASHIMOTO**
CHRISTIAN BAUER, *Tree of Life*
(©UMEX Co., 2007)

15 **ハートボム HEART BOMB**
WRENCH, *feel more* (Cutting Edge, Third culture, 2007)
Director: HEART BOMB
刀匠 Toushou: 藤安将平 Syouhei Fujiyasu
斬手 Zanshu: 修心流居合術兵法 修心館々長 Syuushinryuu Iaijutu Hyouhou,
町井勲 Isao Machii

16 **東弘明 HIROAKI HIGASHI**
BENNIE K, *Endless Summer*

17 **ホッチカズヒロ HOTCHI KAZUHIRO**
DOUDOU (©Hotchi Kazuhiro, 2002)
Director + Animation: ホッチカズヒロ HOTCHI KAZUHIRO
Scenario: サンプラザ中野 Sunplaza Nakano
アニマ *Anima* (©Hotchi Kazuhiro, 2005)
Director + Animation: ホッチカズヒロ HOTCHI KAZUHIRO
Music: 松田眞樹 Maki Matsuda

18 **市村幸卯子 YUKO ICHIMURA**
`P` out of Licca• SWEET AND SPICE DVD (©2007 Tomy)
Dircctor: 市村幸卯子 Yuko Ichimura (PYRAMID FILM INC.)
Producer: 中島正晴 Masaharu Nakashima (PYRAMID FILM INC.)
DP: 山崎肇 Hajime Yamazaki, Art: 大吉弘晋 Hiroyuki Ohyoshi
SFX: 宮岡俊輔 Shunsuke Miyamoto, MA: 伊藤拓 Taku Ito (PTHREE)
MP: 富永恵介 Keisuke Tominaga (GRANDFNUK Inc.)
Music + Sound Design: Gutevolk
Na: Yukari Fresh, Cast: Licca, Fabulous Bird 5 –YES Sky HI

19 **井上卓 TAKU INOUKE**
JUN 50th Anniversary (©JUN CO.,LTD., 2007)
Director + Animation + SE: 井上卓 Taku Inoue

20 **ケープラスミー K+ME**
K+Me Show Reel (2007)
Director: K+Me

21 **喜田夏記 NATSUKI KIDA**
資生堂 Shiseido, *MAJOLICA MAJORCA web movie / chepter16*
(©Shiseido Co.,Ltd., 2007)

22 **木村敏子 TOSHIKO KIMURA**
Capitol K, *Can't Lie Down*
(©VROOM SOUND RECORDS / ©Faith&Industry, 2005)
Director + Animation: 木村敏子 TOSHIKO KIMURA

23 **木津裕史 HIROSHI KIZU**
椎名林檎×斎藤ネコ『平成風俗大吟醸』DVD Video「ギャンブル」
Ringo Shena × Neko Saito, HEISEI FUZOKU DAIGINJO: DVD VIDEO, *Gambling*
(©EMI Music Japan Inc., 2007)

BNN Bug News Network **DVD** VIDEO ALL 片面一層 MPEG2 字幕無し 複製不能 JASRAC V-0708147 **NTSC** **4:3**

Japanese Motion Graphic Creators' **DVD** | 2008 | Color | 58min. | stereo&mono | ©4D2A

24 古賀学 MANABU KOGA
&a water 01: Guppy (©2007 &a water. Manabu Koga. NORISHIROCKS.)
Director: 古賀学 Manabu Koga, Model: reica, Produce: NORISHIROCKS

25 小嶋貴之 TAKAYUKI KOZYMA
GHEEE, Beautiful stungun (©JULY RECORDS, 2007)
Director: 小嶋貴之 Takayuki Kozyma
田中雄一郎「殴者」Yuichiro Tanaka, Nagurimono (©ground records, 2007)
Director: 小嶋貴之 Takayuki Kozyma

26 くろやなぎてっぺい TEPPEI KUROYANAGI
if time pass (©Teppei Kuroyanagi × Kayaku Project, 2007)
Director: Teppei Kuroyanagi, Dancer: Yannick Hugron (KAYAKU PROJECT)
Kae Kurachi (KAYAKU PROJECT), Editer: Nobutaka Sumiya, Visual effect:
Nobutaka Sumiya, Sound design: Takahide Higuchi, Hair&make: Mizuki Kato,
Camera: Sadaomi Yamada, Satoshi Yamawaki, Title Logo: Makoto Miyakawa,
Digital painter: Makoto Miyakawa, Kazuhiro Tani, Oda Hitoshi Bubuka, Kazumi
Sakagawa, Photographer: Kamu, Special Thanks: Conno, Takeshi Maruyama

27 牧鉄兵 TEPPEI MAKI
OMODAKA, Kokiriko bushi (©Far East recording)
Director + Animation: Teppei Maki

28 水野健一郎 KENICHIRO MIZUNO
「AIBAバリキリー」AIBA BALI KILIE
「静電気」 static electricity
「かけっ子～荒野編」 Kakekko ~ Kouya
「かけっ子～荒野編2」 Kakekko ~ Kouya 2
「ニューファミリー」 New Family

29 水尻自子 YORIKO MIZUSHIRI
「かっぽ」Kappo (©2007 Yoriko Mizushiri)

30 村越陽平 YOHEI MURAKOSHI
BLOCKMAN (2008)
Director + Animation: 村越陽平 YOHEI MURAKOSHI

31 永田ナヲミ NAOMI NAGATA
中山二葉「砂と女の子」Futaba Nakayama, Suna to Onnanoko
(©Alchemy Records, 2007)
Director + Animation: 永田ナヲミ NAOMI NAGATA
Music: 中山双葉 Futaba Nakayama

32 モンノカヅエ＋ナガタタケシ
TAKESHI NAGATA, KAZUE MONNO
PIKA PIKA 2007 (©2007 TOCHKA)

33 中尾浩之 HIROYUKI NAKAO
オリジナルドラマ「ZERO」DVDティザー
Original Drama ZERO, DVD Teaser
(©2008 Zero Partners)

34 西郡勲 ISAO NISHIGORI
ACIDMAN, Walking Dada (©EMI Music Japan Inc., 2007)

35 野本大 NOMOTO MASARU
「バックドロップ・クルディスタン」
Back Drop Kurdistan (Back Drop Film, 2007)
Director: 野本大 NOMOTO MASARU

36 大原大次郎 DAIJIRO OHARA
SAKEROCK「ぐうぜんのきろく2」Guzen no Kiroku2
Opening Animation (©KAKUBARHYTHM, 2007)
Director + Animation: 大原大次郎 Daijiro Ohara

37 オンナコドモ ONNACODOMO
A Guide Tour of onnacodomo
(©onnacodomo, 2008)

38 大月壮 SOU OOTSUKI
BROSTA TV AWARD 2008 (©BROSTA TV)

39 OTAS
MONTAGE 2008 (2007 OTAS.TV)

40 志賀匠 TAKUMI SHIGA
二千花 Nichika, Genius Party (©R and C Ltd., 2007)

41 島田大介 DAISUKE SHIMADA
ウリチパン郡「ゼノン」Urichipan-Gun, Zenon
(©AKICHI RECORDS)
Director: Daisuke Shimada

42 新海岳人 TAKETO SHINKAI
Yama to Hito (short.ver) (©Taketo Shinkai, 2007)
Director: Taketo Shinkai

43 ソライロ SORAIRO
horizon (©Sorairo, 2008)

44 菅原そうた SOTA SUGAHARA
ミラクルネットショッピング「イスコプター篇」
Miracle Net Shopping, Isucopter (©Tonio Pro, 2008)
「キモちゃん」Kimo-chan (©Tonio Pro, 2008)

45 須藤カンジ KANJI SUTO
LEO IMAI, Gaining Weight (EMI Music Japan Inc.)

46 田尾創樹 SOJU TAO
おかめはちもく「あの娘の瞳は螺旋状」
Okamehachimoku, Anokono Hitomi ha Rasenjou (2007)
Camera: 岩橋健太郎 Kentaro Iwabashi

47 辻川幸一郎 KOICHIRO TSUJIKAWA
Cornelius, Fit Song (©WARNER MUSIC JAPAN INC., 2007)
Director: Koichiro Tsujikawa, CG: Munechika Inudo
Cornelius, Like a Rolling Stone (©WARNER MUSIC JAPAN INC., 2007)
Director: Koichiro Tsujikawa
Cornelius, Omstart (©WARNER MUSIC JAPAN INC., 2007)
Director: Koichiro Tsujikawa, CG: Tsugutaka Fukuoka

48 山口崇司 TAKASHIYAMAGUCHI
d.v.d「01 > 01」seek the planet no.8 (HEADZ, 2007)

49 吉浦康裕 YASUHIRO YOSHIURA
「イヴの時間」The Time of EVE
(©Yasuhiro YOSHIURA / DIRECTIONS, INC. 2008)
Director: Yasuhiro YOSHIURA , Animation: Yasuhiro YOSHIURA + Directions

INTRODUCTION

本書『映像作家100人』は、日本の映像作家年鑑です。映像というジャンルで、優れた表現を行っている作家100人を選りすぐり、彼らのプロフィールと作品を掲載しています。

スクリーンの裏側で、誰がどのように新しい映像を作り出しているのか。それを追いかけて、この本はミュージックビデオの世界から、CM、アニメーション、インタラクティブアート、ドキュメンタリーの世界までを横断してきました。映像と一口に言っても、それが包含する領域は、すでにカテゴライズしきれないほど広く拡大しています。映像作家たちは、街頭ビジョン、インターネット、携帯端末、そして実際に触れることのできる作品に至るまで、次々とブラウン管という枠組みを突き破り、新しい領域へ進もうとしています。本書では、そうした現状を踏まえ、斬新なビジュアルイメージを抽出するだけではなく、今の映像表現を幅広く俯瞰しています。映像を用いて人々が可能性を切り開いていく、その地図のようなものをこの本を読んで感じてもらえたらと思います。

2008年度版となる本書は、通算3冊目の発行となります。これまでも数多くの作家たちを掲載してきましたが、今年はより若い作家たちが登場しています。若い年齢のクリエイターたちが縦横無尽に活躍できるのも、この映像というジャンルの特徴かもしれません。映像関連の技術が安価で誰にでも使えるものになりつつあることも一因と言えますが、それだけではなく、映像というジャンル自体がまだ若く、誰も行っていない仕事がまだそこに多く残されていることがその大きな要因かもしれません。新しいアイデアと才能に、まだまだ映像という世界の門戸は、開かれているのです。本書は、そんな若い才能へ仕事を発注したいクライアントのために、作家たち全員の連絡先を掲載し、また一部の作品を付録のDVDに収録しています。この本が、新しい才能を見つけ出すガイドブックとなれば、そう願っています。

100人という作家数は、映像というジャンルの広がりからすれば、ほんの一部に過ぎません。そのかわり、100人の内の半数以上が今年初めて掲載される作家たちで占められています。現在活躍しているクリエイターはもちろんですが、新しい領域で実験的な活動している作家を収録しているのは、これから映像というジャンルが進んで行く未来を、彼らが全身で体現していると思うからです。この1年の間にも、無数のクライアントと作家たちの組み合わせから、さまざまな映像が生み出されました。彼らのユニークな仕事もダイジェストのように楽しんでいただけたらと思います。最後に、作家の選定に掲載に惜しみなく協力していただいた方々、本書に掲載されているすべての映像作家たち、この書籍の制作に関わっていただいた方々に感謝を捧げたいと思います。

"Japanese Motion Graphic Creators" is an annual of motion graphic creators. We selected a group of 100 creators whose expression in the field of motion graphics is outstanding, and their profiles and works appear here.

"Behind the screen" - where do they work and what kind of things are making? In pursuing these questions, this book travels from the world of music video through the worlds of commercials, stop-motion animation, interactive art and documentary. The realm comprising "motion graphics" is no longer reasonably capable of being categorized, and we use a broad definition of the term. Works that function as "motion graphics" include large-scale public screens, internet, PDAs, and even works that one can actually touch. The limits of the cathode-ray tube have been destroyed, and we are entering a new universe. Based on that state of affairs, the present volume not only samples original images, but also broadly surveys motion graphics of the present. In so doing, we would like for you to appreciate this book as a kind of map to what kind of possibilities people employing the medium of motion graphics are carving out.

This 2008 edition numbers the 3rd volume so far. This year those represented are generally younger. These kinds of young creators can do their work freely, and perhaps that is a particular feature of the field of motion graphics. One might say that things like the cheaper cost of motion graphic-related technology are also factors. But it's not only that. The field of motion graphics itself is still young, most remaining work is still something that no one has ever seen, which might be the number one reason that young geniuses spring up one after the next. The entryway to the world of motion graphics is still expanding for new ideas and geniuses. In order for clients to order jobs from the young geniuses in this book, the contact information of all of them is included, and some works are included in the attached DVD. We hope for this book to become a guidebook discover these young geniuses.

Thinking of the expanse of motion graphic genres that this books deals with, the number of 100 creators is merely a single portion. In exchange, more than half of the creators are introduced for the first time this year. There is a particular emphasis on young creators, and especially those forging new territory. It is true of course for creators that are active now, but the reason for including experimental creators who are doing work in new areas is because they embody with their whole beings the future of progress in motion graphics. This past year too, from a countless number of combinations of clients and creators, a myriad of visuals were created. Please enjoy reading this book as a summery of this year's motion graphics.

映像制作の現場

BEHIND
THE SCENE
012-031

スクリーンの裏側にいる映像作家たち。
その制作・発表現場を訪ねた。

文／林永子（013,018,024,030）
古屋蔵人（014,017,029） 庄野祐輔（021,022,026）

ステージにはシンメトリーに置かれた2台のドラム。ど真ん中にはラップトップ。セットだけでもかなりのインパクト、奇抜な雰囲気を醸し出しているというのに、背後に控えるプロジェクターがなにやら事件の予感。ライブが始まる前の一時、一筋縄ではいくはずもないセッティングを前にしたオーディエンスは期待に胸を膨らませながら、今か今かとメンバーを待ち受ける……。

映像と音が完全に同期した驚異のパフォーマンスで音楽、映像、さらにはアート界をも震撼させる新型トリオといえば、『d.v.d』。個性派ドラムデュオItoken + Jimanicaを左右に従え、中央のPCを巧みに操るのは映像作家の山口崇司。DrumsとVisualとDrumsで「d.v.d」です、よろしくプリーズ！

彼らの編み出した音と映像のリンクパフォーマンスは、事前に作った映像素材を再生するVJスタイルとは訳が違う。ピンボールのゲーム画面が映し出されると、まずはVisual担当山口がWiiのリモコンを操作してボールを投入。左右対象

に配置されたフリッパーはドラムを叩く音に反応し、ドラム2人はボールが落ちないよう連打する。楽曲はすべて「音が映像を動かし、映像が曲を奏でる」。前人未到のインタラクティブ・パフォーマンスは「ライヴインスタレーション」と呼ばれ、昨年行われたアート展「六本木クロッシング」を筆頭に、現代アートシーンでも人々の度肝を抜くことになった。

メンバーは個別の活動でも活躍中。ソロドラマーとして様々なユニットに参加するItokenとJimanica。山口崇司は映像作家として、プログラミングを絡めた作品、インタラクションデザイン、グラフィックデザインなどを手がけている。そもそもが自由、あまりにも独特な個性を持った3人が組めば、独特ぶりもより強烈に、何もかもが型破りなトリオロジーの出来上がり。昨年11月には『d.v.d』のデビューアルバム「01 > 01 (01 Less Than 01)」をDVDリリースし、ヨーロッパツアーも堂々敢行。革新的な確信犯、d.v.dが世界を席巻する日は近い！

Two drum sets placed symmetrically on the stage. And a laptop in between. Merely the set alone has quite an impact, and despite the fact that a strange atmosphere is produced, the projector which is held back in the rear for some reason portends something ominous. In the time before the show begins, the audience is filled with excited anticipation at this set-up that shouldn't reasonably work out, waiting and thinking "Are they coming out yet? Are they on their way...?" If you want a new type of trio that rocks the worlds of music, motion graphics and moreover art with prodigious performances, where the visuals and sound are synchronized, then D.V.D is that trio. With the unique drum duo of Itoken and Jimanica on either side, the motion graphic creator in the center manning the PC with such facility is Takashi Yamaguchi. "Drums + Visual + Drums" = "D.V.D". Please enjoy our show! The purpose behind this method of "link performing" with sound and visuals worked out at the same time, is different from that of the style of VJs who project footage that has been previously prepared. If a pinball game appears on the screen, first Mr. Yamaguchi, in charge of visuals, uses the Wii remote to launch the ball. The flippers placed on the left and right react to the sound of the drums, and the two drummers pound drum rolls to keep the ball from falling down. The whole piece is made up of sounds making visuals move and visuals "playing" music. This unprecedented interactive performance is a "live installation", and starting from an appearance at last years "Roppongi Crossing" exhibition, they have become an astounding feature on the contemporary art scene.
The individual members are also involved in their own projects. Itoken and Jimanica participate in varied groups as solo drummers. As a motion graphic creator, Takashi Yamaguchi undertakes programming-related work, as well as work involving things like interaction design or graphic design. Of free natures to begin with, and all 3 members being extremely and particularly individual, when they join forces, they become even more intense, and everything is made into an unconventional "triology". They released their debut DVD album "01 > 01 (01 Less Than 01)" last November and embarked on a magnificent tour of Europe. The day is at hand when the innovative ideological criminals d.v.d will sweep the globe!

01

D.V.D

渋谷のNHKほど近くの映像制作会社の一室。オレンジに塗られた腰ほどの高さのセットが半円状にくり抜かれている。そこから顔を出しているのは糸操り人形師の結城一糸。絡まった10数本の糸をほどくのに悪戦苦闘している。大音量が鳴り響く狭い室内にはライティングスタッフ、撮影スタッフ、制作スタッフ、ミュージシャン所属事務所のスタッフなど総勢20人近くがひしめいていて、肌寒い季節にもかかわらず汗が出るほどの熱気に包まれている。ここは若手映像ディレクター長添雅嗣によるDJ BAKUのミュージックビデオの撮影現場。

長添は若干28歳にしてすでに多くの実績と、確かな評価を得た映像作家だ。映像作品としての企画とアイデアはもちろん、グラフィックデザイン的なセンスの高さも持ち合わせた、数少ない作家の一人で、実際に彼は武蔵野美術大学卒業後、デザイナーとして映像制作会社teevee graphicsに参加している。やがて、いくつかのミュージックビデオを手が

ける機会を得て、そこからトントン拍子に映像作家としてのキャリアを重ねてきた。彼は、しっかりと美しく映像を仕上げる職人気質と、この自身を包んでいたPAMのカラフルなセーターのようなポップセンスで映像世界をカタチにする。

やがて絡まった糸をほどききった結城が巧みに人形を操り出し、無表情だった木の人形が魂が入ったようになめらかに演じ出す。人形は手に握った大きなスタンプを机に向かって押し続ける。ディレクターが大きな声で人形の感情を代弁する。「あーっ、ハンコが勝手に動く！」その絶叫に応じて人形が持つスタンプがまるで人形の意思から分離したように宙を舞う。不思議と人形がうろたえたように見えてくる。

今回のプロジェクトでは予算のほとんどを人形制作にあてたのだという。長添はたびたびこういう姿勢で仕事に臨む。予算にかかわらず常に高い理想を持って映像に取り組み、限られた条件の中で最高の絵をつくることにこだわり続けている。

A room in a motion graphics company in Shibuya near NHK. The waist-high wall of the set is painted orange, and made in a semicircle with a hole in the middle. From the hole, string puppeteer Yuki Ishi puts out his head as he struggles to unravel more than 10 entangled strings. Loud music is reverberating in this tiny room crammed with a staff of about 20 people. Writing, photography, production and art staff are all in a feverish state of concentration, sweating despite the chilly season. This is where young director Masatsugu Nagasoe is filming a music video for DJ Baku.
At 28, Nagasoe is a motion graphic creator who has already demonstrated many achievements and received decided acclaim. He is a creator of few works, blending a high level of good taste in motion graphic production with of course his discerning taste in graphic design. In fact, after graduating from Musashino Art University, he started working as a director for the motion graphics production company Tee Vee Graphics. Before long he was afforded the opportunity to work on music videos and his career began its rapid ascent. With his pride in the craftsmanship of creating visuals in a

dedicated and beautiful way, and just like the colorful Pam sweater he is wrapped in today, he projects a vivid visual world.
Presently the puppeteer has unraveled the string and dexterously begun making the dolls move, effortlessly extracting a performance out of the expressionless wood that makes the dolls seems as if they in fact had souls. The dolls are grabbing big stamps and pressing them on a table. The director is expressing their feelings for them in a loud voice, "Oh! The stamps are moving all on their own!" And it is just so; the stamps dance suspended in the air as if completely disconnected from the will of the dolls. And fantastically, we begin to see the dolls as being thrown into a state of panic.
The actual budget of this project was basically only the cost of filming, in other words the creation of the dolls was the main commitment. The truth is that he frequently prefers this approach to his work. He pursues his visuals with consistently high ideals, irrespective of the budget, and obsesses about making excellent pictures within whatever limitations.

02

長添雅嗣
MASATSUGU NAGASOE

CG作家の菅原そうたに創作風景を撮影させて欲しいと依頼したところ"競艇場"まで連れて行ってくれるという。

品川駅で待ち合わせ、彼の車で学芸大前に向かい、バーミヤンで彼の師匠にあたるタナカカツキをピックアップし、平和島競艇場のタワーパーキングに車を停めた。近所のスーパーで67円の食パンを50袋ほど買い占めた彼らは、ボートレースには目も向けず、競艇場裏手の橋で両手に抱えたビニール袋を下ろした。

2人の出会いは前世紀末、タナカカツキのCGアニメーション制作チームとして集められた、通称「カツキ塾」がきっかけ。当時見いだされたスタッフには大月壮、牧鉄兵、そして菅原そうたという強烈な若手が揃っていた。タナカカツキは手荒で、勢い任せなCGに定評のある菅原作品を「バカCG」とカテゴライズすることによって、菅原の個性とスタンスを明確化した。

橋の上でハンディカムを回しながら、食パンの袋を片っ端から開け始めた2人はパンを小さくちぎり、次の瞬間それを川に向かって放り投げた。すると数匹のカモメが空中を旋回

し出す。どんどんとパンを投げ入れ続ける2人、空中を旋回する鳥の数がみるみるふくれあがっていく。後ろを走る幹線道路のノイズに包まれていた橋は、鳥の羽音と「ぎゃー」という鳴き声で溢れかえる。

彼らは普段からこうして時折2人で「遊び撮影」をしたり、お互いのアニメーションやCG素材を交換し合って作品を作っているのだという。誰に見せるというわけでもない、特に発表する予定のない、創作意欲を満たすだけの創作である。

鳥が集まりきったところで菅原そうたが奇声を発しながら大きな食パンを投げ入れた。「ぎゃあ！ぎゃあ！ぎゃあ！」放られた食パンに向かってカモメが一斉に突進していき、川辺を中心にした空間がものすごいテンションに包まれる。自転車を停めてその場を観察していたご老人も嬉しそうに白い歯をのぞかせている。

結局40袋ほどを投げ、鳥レイヴを盛り上げきった彼らは力尽き、残りのパンを橋桁のホームレスに寄贈して、その場をあとにした。

When we asked CG creator Sota Sugawara to let us film him at work shooting, he ended up bringing us to a motorboat racetrack.
Meeting us at Shinagawa Station, we went in the direction of Tokyo Gakugei University, picking up his teacher Katsuki Tanaka at Bamiyan, and parking the car in the Heiwajima Motorboat Racetrack Tower lot. They bought up 50 packages of sliced bread for 67 yen each in the local supermarket, and without even looking at the race, they put the plastic bags they were holding under his arms on the bridge behind the track.
The two met at the end of the last century, on the occasion of the formation of a creative team called "Katsuki Juku" ("Katsuki's school"), put together for the CG-animation. The staff he found for himself were the intense and young Sou Otsuki, Teppei Maki, and Sota Sugawara. Katsuki Tanaki clarified Sugawara's individuality and style by categorizing his works as "silly CG", since he is famous for being bad in his execution of CG modeling and movement.
While filming with a handicam, the two open the bags of bread on the bridge one after the next, and break the

bread into little pieces, which in the next instant they toss into the river. At that point a few seagulls begin circling overhead. They continue throwing in more and more bread, and the number of circling birds swells in no time at all. This bridge, which is wrapped with the noise of the highway that runs behind it, is now inundated with the sounds of flapping wings and bird cries.
This is how these two create; by doing things like sometimes having a kind of "play" shooting, or exchanging animation and CG footage. It's not that they will show it to anyone or release it. This is creation for the sake of satisfying the need to create.
When the birds have finished gathering, Sugawara throws a big piece of bread in while uttering a strange sound. All the seagulls dive down together towards the tossed bread and the space around the riverside is wrapped in fantastic excitement. An elderly man has stopped his bike and is showing us his white teeth in joy at watching the scene.
After using up about 40 bags, these two who fired up a "bird rave", are tired out, and they give away the rest of the bread to the homeless under the bridge.

03

菅原そうた
SOTA SUGAHARA

暗闇をキャンバスにライトで落書き。発光体のストローク
は長時間露光によって1コマ1コマ撮影され、連続再生する
ことによって光のアニメーションへと生まれ変わる……。

ライトをモチーフに、遊び心満載の幻想的な映像作品を
作り出すのは、ナガタタケシとモンノカヅエによる映像
ユニット、トーチカ。ミュージックビデオや映画予告編、
「UNIQLO JUMP!」（2007年）などの企業広告を手がける2
人だが、代表作品はなんといっても光のアニメーション作品
「PiKAPiKA」である。

図形、人型、花、抽象的なストロークが闇に浮かび上が
る、楽しく美しい「PiKAPiKA」は、オタワ国際アニメーショ
ン映画祭特別賞や文化庁メディア芸術祭アニメーション部門
賞を受賞。今年2月に行われた世界最大の短編映画祭、クレ
ルモンフェラン国際短編映画祭では、「Pikapika, Lightning
Doodle Project」がLabo部門グランプリ受賞の栄誉に輝い
た。メディアからの注目もさることながら、その実験的な手
法はコアな映像ファンから子供たちまで、世界中の人々の好

奇心を捕らえて離さない。

「PiKAPiKA」は今年、So-netと共に「世にも不思議で美
しい"光"のプロジェクト」を立ち上げた。ブログ(http://
pikapikaproject.blog.so-net.ne.jp)では、プロジェクト参
加者による「PiKAPiKA」創作活動、「あなたにもできる！超カ
ンタン『PiKAPiKA』の作り方」などをレポート。見ているう
ちに自分も友達や家族を誘って『PiKAPiKA』メイキングにト
ライしたくなってくる。また、3月7日には「PiKAPiKA THE
MOVIE ~Go! Go! PiKAPiKA!!~」を公開。初めてストーリー
性を取り入れたという作品の内容はもちろん、同ブログにてレ
ポートされている制作現場のメイキングも一見の価値がある。

『PiKAPiKA』はモニターの中に収まる「作品」を見るに留ま
らず、ワークショップで体験することもできる。会場を訪れ
た来場者がペンライトを握り、思い思いの図柄を落書きする
様子を撮影。アニメーション化された映像を目の当たりにし
た参加者は驚きと感動の声をあげる。あなたも光のお絵描き
にチャレンジしてみては？

Scribbling darkness on canvas using light. Luminous strokes
photographed on long exposure one frame at a time, when
replayed in sequence, are reborn as "light" animation...

Takeshi Nagata and Kazue Monno are Tochka, a motion
graphics unit that uses light as a motif, making magical works
full of playful spirit. They have worked on music videos,
movie trailers and things like the commercial advertisement
"UNIQLO JUMP!" (2007); their magnum opus is the "light"
animation "PiKAPiKA".

The fun and beautiful "PiKAPiKA", in which graphic shapes,
humanoids, flowers and abstract strokes emerge from the
dark, won a special prize at the Ottawa International Animation
Festival and the animation prize at the Japan Media Arts
Festival. "Pikapika, Lightning Doodle Project" shines with the
honor of having won the Labo Grand Prize this past February
in the Clermont-Ferrand International Short Film Festival, the
largest short film festival in the world. Receiving attention
from the media as well, Tochka's core experimental methods

have grabbed the curiosity of people around the world, from
movie fans to children, and won't let go.

This year PiKAPiKA started a project with So-net to bring the
"marvelous beautiful 'light' to the world". On their blog (http://
pikapikaproject.blog.so-net.ne.jp) there are reports about
how anyone can quite easily make "PiKAPiKA". Watching it
makes you not only try making PiKAPiKA yourself, but also
call your family and friends. And on March 7th, "PiKAPiKA
THE MOVIE ~Go! Go! PiKAPiKA!! ~" came out. Details about
this work (which is their first to introduce a story) including
on-location making-of reports are also worth having a look
at on the blog.

"PiKAPiKA" may be experienced not only trapped inside a
monitor as a "work", but also in a workshop. Those who come
to the venue grip penlights, and their freely-made doodles
are then filmed. Participants are excitedly moved when they
witness the animated result. How would you too like to try
drawing your own "light" animation?

04

TOCHKA

ユーフラテスは、慶応義塾大学 佐藤雅彦研究室から生まれたクリエイティブ・グループ。佐藤研究室は、CM、ゲーム、映画など様々な表現を手がける佐藤雅彦が慶応義塾大学へ着任する際に組織したもので、主な活動は、表現方法および教育方法の研究である。同研究室の卒業生からなるユーフラテスの仕事場は、ものを生み出す工房でありながら、専門書の輪読や科学実験なども行われる大学の研究室のような場所。そこには、アイデアのメモが書かれた黒板、そして過去の作品で使用した装置の一部、あるいは研究に使われたオブジェのようなものなどが整然と置かれていた。その場所から生み出される彼らの作品は、どれもが非常に明快で、新鮮なアイデアに溢れている。それは、彼らが映像のビジュアル面やストーリーテリングの側面からではなく、ものづくりの考え方そのものにアプローチするためだ。その制作姿勢には、何か

を作り出す「制作」という行為と、その過程にある仕組みを考える「研究」という行為の、2つの姿勢が共存している。それは、彼らが研究室を母体として生まれたという、映像クリエイターとしては特異な経歴からきているのかもしれない。

そんな彼らが注目されたのは、制作スタッフを務めるNHKの教育番組「ピタゴラスイッチ」だった。そこから彼らの快進撃は続く。2007年、ニューヨークADCで、ISSEY MIYAKEのWebと店頭で放映された短編映像「A-POC INSIDE.」がGold Awardを、大日本印刷の新社屋のために作られたアニメーション作品「イデアの工場」がMerit Awardを受賞した。真心ブラザーズの「きみとぼく」や、「All I want to say to you」のミュージックビデオなども手がけている。そのすべてに、ユーフラテスならではのアイデアが貫かれ、見るものに新しい驚きを与えている。

Euphrates is a creative group born out of the Masahiko Sato Keio University Laboratory. The Laboratory is involved in varied types of expression including commercials, games and movies, and was created when Masahiko Sato took up his position at Keio University, hence their research is mainly in methods of expression, and methods of education. The workplace of those who graduate from the Laboratory is at once a factory for developing things, as well as being a kind of university research facility for studying specialized literature and doing scientific experiments. Neatly organized and available there are a blackboard with ideas jotted down, parts of devices used in older works, and curios used in the Laboratory. The works of art that they produce are every one extremely lucid and brimming over with fresh ideas. This does not come from the side of motion graphic visuals storytelling, but it is because of their artisan's approach to thinking about things. There are 2 approaches coexisting; the act of "creating"

in order to produce something, and the act of "researching" by which one thinks about the mechanism of the ideas in the process. This might be because they were "raised" in the Laboratory and have a different background from most motion graphic creators. What gained attention for them was the program "Pythagoras Switch" which they created as staff for NHK Educational TV. And from there their success continued. In 2007 the short film "A-POC inside" which they made for ISSEY MIYAKE's website and stores, won the ADC Gold Award in New York and the animation work "Factory of Ideas" made for Dai Nippon Printing's new company building won the Merit Award. They have also handled music videos such as the Magokoro Brothers "Kimi to Boku" and "All I want to say to you". Behind all of it, anything by Euphrates is penetrated at the back by the thought process of the Laboratory and they transmit a new kind of excitement to the things we are looking at.

05

EUPHRATES

onnacodomoは、最近自身のファーストアルバム「Today」をリリースしたばかりのDJ codomoと、アニメーション作家のせきやすこ、イラストレーターの野口路加をメンバーとするVJユニット。VJといっても、自作のCG映像やサンプリング映像をミックスするこれまでのVJとは全く違う、レコーディングされた素材をまるで使わないVJである。VJの素材として登場するのは、キッチン用品といった日用品から、折り紙やホログラムシート、おみやげ品のようなB級アイテムまで、どこでも誰にでも手に入るようなものばかり。今回は、そんな彼らのセッティングを上から撮影。こんな、色とりどりのがらくたのようなものを、彼らは虫眼鏡や水槽などを使ったお手製のエフェクトで面白い形に見せたり、フレームを拡大して切り取って見せたりする。その過程をそのままビデオでリアルタイムに撮影し投影するというのが彼らのVJシステムだ。

彼らの作品には、何か形をなさなければというがんばりとか、表現してやろうという力みがまるでない。それはただそこにあるものを自然と利用して作られている。偶然に生まれてくる映像を、そのままの姿として楽しむ。せつないほど簡単・シンプルな方法で作られる世界の印象は、たとえば万華鏡をのぞいて思い出すようなことに似ている。それは、実際は意識に登らないこと、よく目をこらせば、この世界のかけらが思いのほか美しいということ、そして、耳を澄ませば聞こえてくる音はもっとゆたかで様々であるということを思い出させてくれる。

どうやって作っているのか想像もつかないような、高度な技術を使って作られるCGアニメーションや、完璧な照明と作りこまれたセットで生み出される完成されたミュージックビデオの世界とは、対極にある彼らの表現フォーマット。でもそれは、だからこそとても新鮮で、過激なのだ。

onnadocomo is a VJ unit made up of DJ codomo, a DJ who recently released his first album "Today", animator Yasuko Seki and illustrator Ruka Noguchi. Even though they are called a "VJ unit", they are not like other VJs who mix things like original CG footage and sampled footage, and they in fact use no pre-recorded materials at all. The kinds of materials that make an appearance are all things that anyone can get their hands on anytime, like kitchen utensils (everyday utensils), folding paper, hologram sheets and cheap tchotchkes. This time we took a photo of their set-up on. They use hand-made effects like magnifying glasses and aquariums to show all this varied junk in an interesting way, magnifying and diminishing the frame.
Their VJ system is to film a process and project it just as it is. There is no sense of some kind of determination for something to gather shape, or the strain to express themselves; they create merely by naturally using what they find. Not a collage, but a "chance operation" or something like a "cut-up". And the visuals that are born from this process are exciting to view just as they are. Our impression of a world made using this almost painfully simple method resembles something like a recollection triggered by glancing into a kaleidoscope. This is something that doesn't make it to our consciousness, in other words, if we peel our eyes, the shards of this world remind us of beauty beyond our thoughts; if we strain our ears, the sounds we are hearing remind us of things more varied and fertile. Their expressive format is at exactly opposite poles from areas like that of CG animation which uses virtuosic techniques that one can't begin to understand, or the world of music videos that are born complete with perfect lighting and music as a produced set. And this is exactly what's so fresh and radical.

06

ONNACODOMO

時は深夜。目黒のイメージスタジオ109では、とあるCMの撮影準備が行われていた。監督はMV、CM、ショートムービーのディレクションだけでなく、オリジナル作品の制作やアート展への参加など、アーティスト活動も盛んな辻川幸一郎である。

このCMは4月5日よりオンエアされる損保ジャパンのもので、3話完結のシリーズ作品。大きなりんごの木のある丘の上を舞台に、主演の新垣結衣と少年がハートフルな物語を展開させていく。辻川は「見た人が『やさしさ』について考えるようなお話。美しい絵本の世界で出演者の魅力を引き出したい」と、撮影前に意欲を見せる。

コンセプトは、セットで作るリアルな絵本。2日間の撮影で3パターンすべてを撮影する予定とあり、早いペースでのセット転換が必要となってくる。そんな過酷なスケジュールであっても、辻川の目に映る大掛かりなセットは「大きなプラモデル」。「男の子としては最高の体験（笑）」と目を輝かせる。

CM制作そのものの面白さについても、興味深い話を聞か

せてもらった。「クライアントの意向や、代理店のクリエイティブディレクターさんの企画など、いろいろな条件がある環境で、自分自身でコントロールできない、予想外の作品が生まれるところが面白い。制約のない自由な条件での表現は、逆に自己にとらわれて自分の世界だけで終わってしまうことも多いのですが、CMは思いがけない出会い、発見がある。自分とは無関係の事情によって決められた方向性や、条件を満たすために真摯に取り組んでも、どうしても消せない何かが無意識の内に残ってしまう。それこそが作品の個性になっている気がするし、面白いところです」。年間に大量の仕事をこなしている辻川は、大勢の人とのセッションを要する仕事で自己を再発見していくようだ。

今後の予定も多方面に。「その都度の流れでいろいろと活動していきたい。1つのジャンルに凝り固まりたくはないんです」。ますます広がっていく彼の活動に、今後も目が離せない。

辻川幸一郎
KOICHIRO TSUJIKAWA

It's the small hours of the night. In Image Studio 109 Meguro Studio 109, preparations are being made for the shooting of a certain commercial. The director, Koichiro Tsujikawa, is someone who is not only involved in things like music videos, commercials and short movies, but who also makes his own original works, takes part in art exhibitions etc, and is thriving as an artist.

This Sompo Japan commercial to be broadcast from April 5th, is a work in 3 segments. On a hill with large apple trees, Yui Aragaki and a young boy act out a heart-warming story. Tsujikawa intends for those who watch it to think about kindness, and he shows us before shooting his desire to draw out the charm of these actors in a beautiful picture-book world.

The concept is a "real picture-book" made on a set. With the goal of filming all 3 patterns over the course of 3 days, the quick changing of the set becomes important. Even on such a tough schedule, Tsujikawa's impression is that the big plastic model is the most ambitious set. His eyes are gleaming because this is just the kind of things that boys like!

He also told us about his fascination with commercials.

Within the boundaries of all the various conditions, including the needs of the client and the plans of the agent's creative director, he can't control himself, and he gets excited about making something unexpected. In expression free from constraint, one is often overcome by oneself, and usually everything remains within one's own world, but the making of commercials reveals unforeseen meetings and discoveries. Even despite things like a directional orientation based on unrelated provisions, or the serious acceptance of some sort of conditions, no matter what, something inerasable is left behind in our unconscious. It feels like that's exactly where the individual character and interest of this work lies. It seems like Tsujikawa, who has a large volume of jobs every year, rediscovers himself by taking up jobs with a multitude of people.

His current plans go in many directions: "I'd like to be borne along by the demands of each individual job. I don't want my work to fossilize into one given genre." Worth watching more than ever, in his wide variety of activities.

年間200本以上ものCMを手がける映像プロダクション
WOWは、その高いクオリティを誇るアートディレクション
の力と、イメージを形にする確かな技術力により、映像制作
の屋台骨を支えてきた。仙台を出発点とするWOWも、現在
では東京、そしてグローバルに展開するまでに成長した。会
社としての成長を模索しながらも、自主作品の発表や、展覧
会への参加など直接的にお金を生まない活動にも注力を惜し
まない。それは、WOWが仕事と表現の二者択一ではない新
しい会社のあり方をデザインしているからだろう。映像を
作るということを基点としつつも、そこからはみ出してくよ
うなやり方をしているのがWOWの面白いところだ。Tent
Londonで展示した「Tengible」とインタラクティブ映像
「Pattern on Wallpaper」は、そのどちらも映像を介して参
加する人が実際に存在する「物」との新しい関わり方を発見で
きるという装置だった。映像というテクノロジーが、もはや
技術的にこの現実を再現できるほどに進んだ今日、映像と私

たちの間にある境界にこそ表現の探るべき領域が残されてい
るのかもしれない。
　そしてその境界をとうとう越え出てきたのが、この
WOW10というアートブックだった。WOWの「過去10年の
再構築」と、「これからの10年」というテーマに臨んだ本作品
集は、WOWの現在持ちうるすべての力を注ぎ込んだ集大成
ともいえる内容になっている。特筆すべきなのは、本という
形に与えられた、凄まじいまでの素材とそのディテールへの
こだわりだろう。中心に抜かれたOの形に覗いているのは、
印刷ではなく本当の木目である。そこには素材や、その重さ
や軽さ、色彩の効果に至るまで、彼らのデザインに対する研
ぎすまされた意志のようなものが見て取れる。デザインとい
う力によって、映像という抽象的な表現に実際の手触りを与
えること、それがWOWのやろうとしていることなのかもし
れない。これから彼らがどんな可能性を見せてくれるのか。
それが楽しみだ。

The production house WOW, which has been involved
in the creation of more than 200 commercials, has
maintained its backbone of motion graphic production
because of art directors who take pride in high quality,
and because of the solid technical capability to realize
images. Started in Sendai, it is now in Tokyo, and has
grown into a global company. Even as it moves forward
powerfully as a company, it is unsparing in the energy
and money it puts directly even towards projects
that won't make any profit, including the release of
independent works and participation in exhibitions.
Perhaps that is because WOW is designing a new kind
of company that doesn't choose between work and
expression. What makes WOW interesting is their method
of using the creation of motion graphics as a starting
point but then going beyond. Through the devices used
in both "Tengible", and the interactive movie "Pattern on
Wallpaper" which showed at Tent London, the people
who participate can actually discover a new relationship
to "things" through motion graphics. Today, when the
technology of "motion graphics" has come so far that we

can practically reproduce reality, there might be territory
remaining which we ought to probe out in the expression
of the boundary between motion graphics and us.
And then when the boundary was finally surpassed, it
was by an art book called "WOW 10". With the themes
of "the rebuilding of the last ten years of WOW" and
"WOW's next ten years", this is a compilation of works
with all of WOW's potential present power poured into
it. What should be noted are the amazing materials and
details that the book is infused with. Peeping out from
the "O"-shaped center is not something printed, but is
actual wood grain. Here one can see their preference for
maintaining a persistently focused approach to design,
from the materials and the heaviness and lightness, to
the effect of the colors. Perhaps what WOW is trying to
do through these kinds of notions of design is to make
it actually possible to give one the feeling of touching
something abstract like motion graphics. What kinds of
possibilities will they introduce to us in the future? We
can't wait to see.

08

WOW

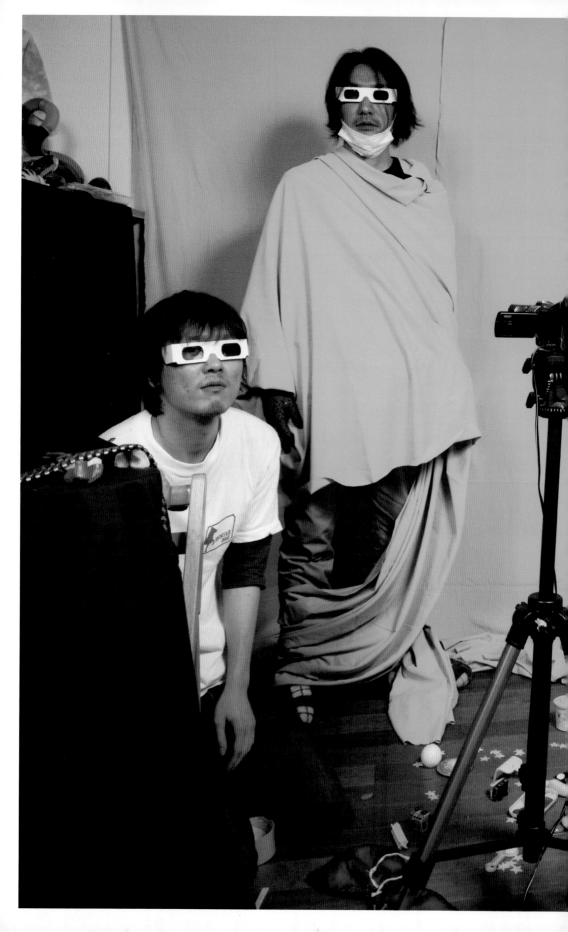

目黒川にほど近い、がらんとしたプレハブのスタジオ。その一角に緑色の布が張り巡らされている。いわゆる合成用のグリーンバック撮影のセット。そのセットの前にはDVカムが据えられ、フロアにはチープなオモチャ、きらきらと光るラメ入りのガジェット、カラフルなプラスチックカップなど、100円ショップにでも売っていそうなガラクタが散りばめられている。

大月壮の映像作家としてのキャリアはまだ3年程度。個性が剥き出しの作品を作るが、手法は固定せずに、一本のミュージックビデオの中ですら、飽き性のように作風をころころと変化させる。実際、アニメーションに始まり静止画、CG動画と様々なタッチが入り交じったAPOGEEの「Just a Seeker's Song」は、そのサービス精神テンコ盛りな映像が大きな話題を呼び、数々のメディアで取り上げられた。

今回制作中の作品はウェブで配信されるアワードのCMで、クライアントからの要望は"特になし、表現手段も尺も一切指定なし、用意された文字要素をちりばめればオーケー"というラフな依頼なのだという、彼にとってこのような自由度の高い仕事はめったにないし、このようなクライアントに出会えることも稀だという。キャリアがわずか数年の、大月

に対する信頼度の高さが窺える。

見るからに個性を炸裂させた作品を作る彼のスタンスは、実はその正反対に「仕事ありき」なのだという。作品作りにおいて自分のエゴを満足させるというよりは、クライアントや視聴者や消費者と向き合って創作しているのだという。

珍しくさしたる指示がないこの仕事に対しては「とにかく遊びながら作る」、100円ショップで買ってきたり、自宅から引っ張り出してきたガラクタをDVカムを前に、アシスタントと談笑しながら泳がせていく。季節の変わり目の風邪に苦しめられマスク姿、グリーンバックで身をくるんだ映像作家は自作自演する。

彼は多くの作家が当然のように目標としている「ハイクオリティ、ハイテクニック」には興味がないのだという。そんなものは過去にもたくさん実現されているし、大手プロダクションに任せておけばよい。クライアントから受けた映像制作依頼、つまり"仕事"の枠組みの中の作業自体にある楽しさ、アイデアを楽しむという姿勢がにじみ出ている。クライアントからのオファーに答えつつ、それでも隠しきれないほどの彼の個性や創作の喜び、それが見る側にとっての"楽しさ"につながるのかもしれない。

A vacant prefab studio fairly near Meguro River. Stretched around one corner of the property is a green piece of cloth. This is what they're calling a set for use in the composition of footage with a green background. A DV camera is set down in front of the set, and cheap toys, sparkling gadgets with mylar, colorful plastic cups, and other junk one might find in a discount store are strewn about the floor.

Sou Otsuki's career as a motion graphic creator is so far about 3 years long. He makes works that aim for a distinct flavor, but his methods are not fixed, and even within one music video he changes from one style to the next as if he had an easily bored disposition.

Actually, the motion graphics for Apogee's "Just a Seeker's Song", starting with animation and having a mix of various approaches that include CG, became well-known for being extremely audience-friendly, and the video was picked up by a number of media outlets.

The piece he is presently working on is a commercial for broadcast on the web. The request from the client is very rough; "We have no particular limits in terms of expressive medium or length, as long as you include the copy we wrote". This makes it a rare job with lots of freedom, encountering such a client is unusual. They are

being quite trusting of this motion graphic creator whose career is only a few years long.

His basic attitude of making works that explode individual personality is in fact unexpectedly quite work-oriented. Instead of satisfying his own ego, he creates work that is in touch with the audience and the consumer.

With respect to this unusual kind of special working without supervision he says "Anyway, we have fun while we work". He and his assistants chat while laying the trinkets from home and from the previous day's discount store excursion in front of the camera. This motion graphic creator's face is enveloped in a white mask because of the cold he caught with the change of season, and his body is wrapped in the green backdrop. He is creating and performing his own work.

He has no interest in the high quality and high technique that so many directors aim for as if they were perfectly natural goals. These kinds of things have been achieved quite often in the past and should be left to major production houses. The fun of the work itself, and the fun of the essential ideas shine through the requirements of the client. The individuality that shines through in response to work done for clients might just be the joy in Otsuki's work.

09

大月壮
SOU OOTSUKI

春一番の吹き荒れた2月某日。都内の撮影スタジオでは、平成のクレイジーキャッツとの呼び声も高いYOUR SONG IS GOODのメンバーがゾンビと死闘を繰り広げていた。

「A MAN FROM THE NEW TOWN」MVの撮影日、総勢30名以上が集結したスタジオは朝から朝まで大賑わい。カットが変わる度に走り回るスタッフの輪の中で、モニターを静かに見つめては指示を出す人物とは、今や押しも押されぬスターディレクター街道をばく進中の田中裕介監督（CAVIAR）である。

田中裕介氏は、平井堅「バイマイメロディー」やAPOGEE「ゴースト・ソング」といったMV、安室奈美恵×VIDAL SASSOON「70年代 Rock Steady」（MV+CM）、マクドナルドのCMなど、様々な映像コンテンツで洗練されたモーションデザインの手腕を発揮してきた。デスクトップ編集世代とあり、美大でグラフィックデザインを学んでいた頃よりモーショングラフィックス制作に着手。CM制作会社に就職して間もなくディレクターデビューを果たし、以降独創的な

ビジュアルアイデアで同世代のミュージシャン、コマーシャル界、映像ファンを魅了し続けている。昨年は20代にしてSPACE SHOWER TV「Music Video Awards」のベスト・ディレクター・オブ・ザ・イヤーを受賞する快挙を成し遂げた。

「A MAN FROM THE NEW TOWN」MVのテーマは「ゾンビvs YOUR SONG IS GOOD」。演奏中のメンバーをゾンビが襲い、メンバーは銃撃で応戦する。大型プロジェクターから投影された様々なシチュエーションのモノクローム素材を背景に、YOUR SONG IS GOODの面々は演技、演奏と大活躍。迫力のバンドショットでは走行車より事前に撮影された町並みがスクリーンに映し出され、楽曲のスーピード感に拍車をかける相乗効果を発揮。また、グラフィカルなデザインを背にしたメンバーそれぞれのショット、団地や町の風景写真の前をルームランナーで歩くシーンなど、静止画と動きの組み合わせの妙技も駆使された。完成したMVは、コミカルながらもシャープな印象が際立つ。その見事なバランス采配に、田中裕介の真骨頂を窺える。

On a certain day in February, when the year's first warm gale blew; in a studio in the city, a deadly struggle is unfolding between members of YOUR SONG IS GOOD (who many people say are like the Heisei Crazy Cats) and the zombies...
Today is the shooting of "A MAN FROM THE NEW TOWN"; there's a huge bustle of activity of a force of more than 30 amassed in the studio from one morning all the way to the next. In the midst of the staff chasing around the room when the shot changes, the person staring quietly at the monitor and giving directions is Yusuke Tanaka (Caviar), who is barreling ahead on the "star director highway".
Yusuke Tanaka has demonstrated an aptitude for sophisticated motion design through his various motion graphic works, including music videos like Ken Hirai's "Bye My Melody", APOGEE'S "Ghost Song", the music video / commercial by Namie Amuro × VIDAL SASSOON, "70's Rock Steady", and McDonald's commercials. In this era of desktop editing, Tanaka undertakes motion graphic creation using the graphic design he learned in art school. After working for a time in an advertising company, he debuted as a director, and continues

those in the commercial world, and motion graphic fans, with his original visual ideas. Entering his 20's last year, he accomplished the feat of winning the Best Director of the Year award on the Space Shower TV Music Video Awards.
The theme of the music video "A MAN FROM THE NEW TOWN" is "Zombies vs. YOUR SONG IS GOOD", the zombies attack the performers and the attack is returned with gunfire. With black and white footage of each situation projected from a massive projector as a background, each member of Your Song is Good gives a stellar performance. Spurred on by the feeling of speed of the song, the synergic effect is achieved through impressive shots of the band gazing at the cityscape filmed from a moving car. And in details like the graphic design that shows up behind the band members in their individual shots and the scene where they walk on treadmills in front of photos of apartment blocks and cityscapes and the like, Tanaka shows his mastery of the skill at merging stills with moving visuals. The completed music video strikes us as being both comical and sharp. The true value of Yusuke Tanaka might be found in the admirable command of that balance.

10

田中裕介
YUSUKE TANAKA

映像作家
クリエイティブファイル

ARCHIVES OF
WORK AND
PROFILE

034-233

阿部伸吾
ABE SHINGO

1981年生まれ。大学卒業後WOWに入社。ディレクター兼デザイナーとしてCM、CI、MVなどを手がける傍ら、外部アーティストとの共同制作、展示などを通して作家活動も積極的に展開。オリジナル作品で2006年RESFEST World Tourに参加、2007年には自ら手がけたCIがPromax & BDA World Gold Award入賞を果たすなど、国内外問わず高い評価を得ている。

1

2

1	MV – THE JETZEJOHNSON, *Dancetek* (©KING RECODS CO., LTD., 2008)	3	CI – *WOWOW 15th* (©WOWOW, 2006)
2	CM – *YAMAHA AT* (©YAMAHA, 2008)	4	VP – *yoshio kubo 2008 spring and summer* (©yoshio kubo, 2007)

BELONG TO	ワウ WOW	CATEGORY	CM, CI, MV, Short Movie
TOOLS	After Effects, CINEMA 4D	TEL / FAX	+81 (0)3 5459 1100 +81 (0)3 5459 1101
		E-MAIL URL	info@w0w.co.jp http://www.abeshingo.com http://www.w0w.co.jp

3

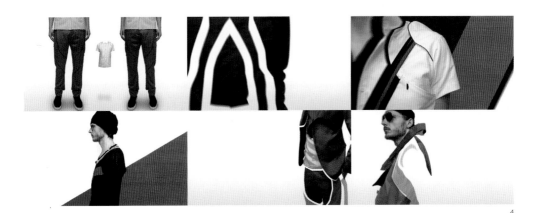

4

Born in 1981. Joined WOW after graduating University. As a director/designer, he collaborates with outside artists and uses exhibitions to actively expand his activities. As for his original works, he was a part of the 2006 RESFEST World Tour, and in 2007 the CI he himself undertook won the Promax & BDA World Gold Award. He is equally respected both domestically and abroad.

AC部
AC-BU

1999年頃、多摩美術大学在学中に結成されたCG＆アニメーション制作トリオ。企画からシナリオ、サウンド、セリフまで、自給自足でまかなうフットワークの軽い制作スタイル。2000年、デジスタアウォード年間グランプリ受賞。以来、テレビ、CM、MV、Webなど様々な映像分野で独自のメソッドによる濃厚ハイテンションなビジュアルを続々投下中。

1

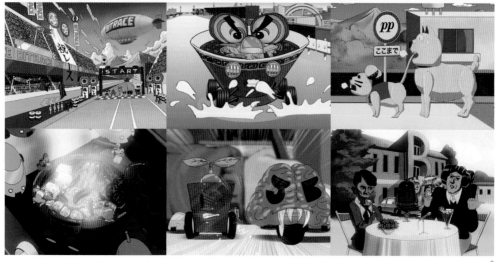

2

1　Short Movie - 海女ゾネス 修行のシーン
   Shugyou Scine from Amazones
   (©AC-bu/Directions, Inc., 2007)

2　TV - 天才テレビくん *Tensai Televi-kun,*
   BIT WORLD, BIT RACER
   (©NHK, 2007)

3　Animation - 分子のナノくん *Bunshi Nano-kun*
   (©RECRUIT CO., LTD., 2007)

4　Short Movie -
   星新一ショートショート劇場「プレゼント」
   Hoshi Shinichi Short Short Gekijo, Present
   (©NHK, 2007)

BELONG TO	AC部	CATEGORY	MV, CM, Short Movie,
	Ac-bu		Animation, TV, Web
TOOLS	Photoshop,	TEL	+81 (0)3-6386-6817
	After Effects,	E-MAIL	info@ac-bu.info
	Final Cut	URL	http://www.ac-bu.info

3

4

A CG and animation production trio founded around 1999 by students at Tama Art University. From production and script-writing to sound and dialogue, they have a versatile self-sufficient style. In 2000 they won the Digista Grand Prize. Using unique methods, they continue to invest dense high-tension visuals in a variety of visual areas including TV, commercials, promotional videos, and web video.

天久聖一
MASAKAZU AMAHISA

1968年生まれ。1989年マンガ家としてデビュー、タナカカツキ氏と共に「バカドリル」などを出版、2003年DDDレーベルより「悲しみジョニー」発売。2004年電気グルーヴのMV「カフェ・ド・鬼」（ピエール瀧監督）でアニメ制作を担当。以後、MVを中心に映像制作を手がける。

A

1 MV – 電気グルーヴ「カフェ・ド・鬼」
Denki Groove, *Cafe de Oni*
(©Ki/oon Records Inc., 2004)

2 MV – 電気グルーヴ「弾けないギターを弾くんだぜ」
Denki Groove, *Hikenai Guitar wo Hikundaze*
(©Ki/oon Records Inc., 2004)

3 MV – ゆらゆら帝国「美しい」
Yura Yura Teikoku, *Utsukushii*
(©Sony Music Associated Records, 2007)

4 MV – 電気グルーヴ「モノノケダンス」
Denki Groove, *Mononoke Dance*
(©Ki/oon Records Inc., 2008)

| TOOLS | After Effects, Final Cut | CATEGORY | MV, CM, Short Movie, Animation |
| | | E-MAIL | amahisam@gmail.com |

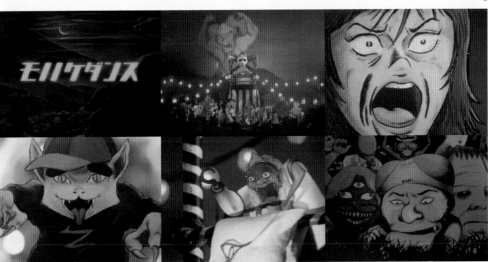

3

4

Born in 1968. Debuting as a comic artist in 1989, he published "Baka Drill" with Katsuki Tanaka, and in 2003 on the DDD label "Kanashimi Johnny". He was in charge of the animation for the Denki Groove video "Café de Oni" (directed by Pierre Taki). Since then his motion graphic creation has focused on music videos.

Art Center College Library
1700 Lida St.
Pasadena, CA 91103

アミカ
AMICA

2007年3月東京工芸大学芸術学部アニメーション学科 "タクゼミ" 卒業。在学中の2006年10月に制作した短編CGアートアニメーション「おはなしの花」が世界中の映画祭で多数の賞を受賞。現在はフリーランスのアートアニメイターとして活動をし、国内外の商業作品やオリジナルのアートアニメーション制作・イラストレーション制作を行っている。

1	Original Animation - 「おはなしの花」 Bloomed Words (©Amica Kubo/Seita Inoue, 2006)	3	Web Animation - Nissan Motor Company Global Website	5	Title Package - VMC
2	Title Package - VMC (JAL)	4	TV Animation - NHK 「あけましてシャキーン!」 Akemashite Shakin!	6	CI Animation - DaiJob.com
				7	TV Title - フジテレビ 「ベビスマ ブリッジ」 Fuji Television Network, Inc., Babysmap Bridge

TOOLS	After Effects, LightWave 3D, Photoshop, Premiere	CATEGORY	MV, CM, Short Animation(TV/Title/Web/etc.), Illustration
		TEL / FAX	+81 (0)3 5842 7300 +81 (0)3 5842 7307
		E-MAIL	infomationbox_01@lovesamical.com
		URL	http://lovesamical.com

A

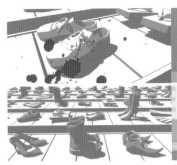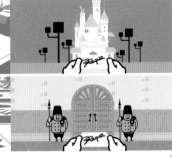

5

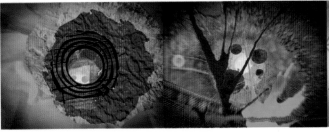

6

7

8

8   DVD Animation - Benesse Worldwide Kids English

A March 2007 arts graduate of the famous "Taku Seminar" at Tokyo Polytechnic University. The CG art animation short "BloomedWords", finished in October of 2006 while still at school, won many prizes around the world. He is now freelance, working not only as an art animator, but also domestically and internationally in commercial work, original art animation work, illustration work, and others.

アンテナ
ANTENNA

京都を拠点に活動中のアートユニット。2002年に結成。メンバー各々が、映像、立体、イラストレーション、建築、デザインなどジャンルを越え横断的に関わり、その可能性によって生み出される新たな表現を目指す。現在のメンバーは田中英行、岡寛志、市村恵介、古川きくみの4人。

1

2

1   Art Film – 「ジャッピー来臨」
    Advent of Jappy
    Director: Hideyuki Tanaka
    Sound: AWAYA
    (Antenna, 2006)

2   Art Film – 「ヤマトピア伝承」
    Legend of Yamatopia
    Director: Antenna
    Sound: Antenna
    (Antenna, 2005)

3   MV – RAM RIDER, *HELLO 8bit edition*
    Director: Hideyuki Tanaka
    (rhythmzone, 2006)

4   MV – AWAYA, *Rainbow Trail*
    Director: Hiroshi Oka
    (AWAYA, 2007)

TOOLS	After Effects, Final Cut, LightWave	CATEGORY	MV, Art Movie, CG Animation, CM
		TEL / FAX	+81 (0)75 381 1189 +81 (0)75 381 1189
		E-MAIL	antennamail@ybb.ne.jp
		URL	http://antennakyoto.com

A

3

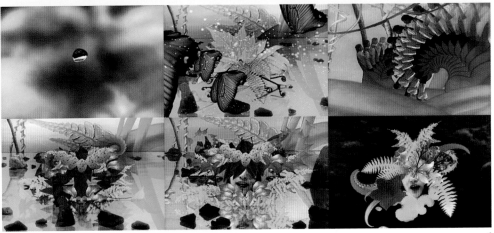

4

Individually, the members' activities transcend genre, including motion graphics, three-dimensional works, illustration, architecture and design, involving themselves in various fields. They seek new what new expressions emerge based on the possibilities of that approach. The present members include Hideyuki Tanaka, Hiroshi Oka, Keisuke Ichimura and Kikumi Furukawa.

006

新井風愉
FUYU ARAI

1979年生まれ。武蔵野美術大学在学中より映像制作を始める。「play」でキャノンデジタルクリエーターズコンテスト2001グランプリ、ベネトンジャパン賞。同2002年、ブロンズ賞。2002年ROBOT入社。とにかくいろいろな映像の企画と演出を手がけて現在に至る。2008年映像ユニット「ふたり」発足。→ www.futari.tv

1   Educational Video–
    ベネッセ Benesse Corporation「Worldwide
    Kids『Mr.Clark』Series Stage 1〜6」
    (©Benesse Corporation, 2007)

2   CM – PASMO「あの街もこの街も篇」
    Anomachimo Konomachimo
    (PASMO Co., Ltd., 2007)

3   Educational Video–
    ベネッセ「おやこえいごほっぷ『COUNT
    1-10』」Benesse Corporation, *Oyako Eigo Hop
    "Count 1-10"*
    (©Benesse Corporation, 2006)

4   Original Works – ふたり Futari,
    HAPPY WEDDING
    (© ふたり (www.futari.tv), 2007)

BELONG TO	ロボット ROBOT	CATEGORY	Short Movie, CM, MV
		TEL / FAX	+81 (0)3 3760 1064 +81 (0)3 3760 1347
TOOLS	After Effects, Logic Pro, Final Cut, Photoshop	E-MAIL URL	arai@robot.co.jp http://www.robot.co.jp http://www.futari.tv

A

2

3

4

Born in 1979. Began making motion graphics while still a student at Musashino Art University. Took the Grand Prize and the Benetton Japan Prize for his work "Play" at the 2001 Canon Digital Creator Contest and won the Bronze Award the following year. Began working at Robot in 2002. In any case he has been involved in various kinds of motion graphics and production. 2008 is the kick-off year for his motion graphic unit "Futari". → www.futari.tv

007

キャドセンター
CAD CENTER CORPORATION

1987年設立。不動産プロモーション静止画／映像、都市計画用VRデータ、展示用インタラクティブコンテンツ制作を中心に、近年は3Dスキャナによる学術用文化財デジタルデータの映像作品化、絵画・版画など美術作品の3Dアニメーション化など、独自のアート系映像を展開。

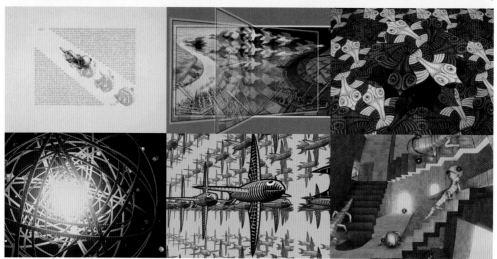

1

2

1　Short Movie - *Venus Venus*
展覧会協力出展（東京藝術大学大学美術館 The University Art Museum - Tokyo National Univ. of Fine Arts and Music, 2006) Director: 大槻一雅 Kazumasa Otsuki, Special Thanks: ルーヴル美術館 The Louvre Museum

2　Short Movie - M.C.Escher, *CONTRAST*
DVD, 一部展覧会協力出展 (Bunkamura ザ・ミュージアム The Bunkamura Museum of Art, 2006) Director: 大槻一雅 Kazumasa Otsuki, All M.C.Escher works ©Escher

Holding B.V.-Baarn-the Netherlands./Huis Ten Bosch-Japan

3　Short Movie - 「PLAN LIBRE/ ル・コルビュジエ 4つの白い住宅 - 絵画＋時間＝建築」
"PLAN LIBRE" Four white houses by Le Corbusier Painting + Time = Architecture
展覧会協力出展（森美術館 the Mori Art Museum, 2007)
書籍『ル・コルビュジエ展 建築とアート、その創造の軌跡 展覧会記録』付属 DVD に収録
Director: 橋本 拓 Taku Hashimoto

Planning + Production: キャドセンター CAD CENTER, 森美術館 Mori Art Museum
Special Thanks: Fondation Le Corbusier

4　Short Movie - Odilon Redon, *NOIR*
DVD, 一部展覧会協力出展 (Bunkamura ザ・ミュージアム The Bunkamura Museum of Art, 2007) Director: 大槻一雅 Kazumasa Otsuki
作品所蔵：岐阜県美術館 THE MUSEUM OF FINE ARTS, GIFU

TOOLS	CINEMA 4D, After Effects, Final Cut, etc...	CATEGORY	3DCG Animation/ Illustration, MV, VR Contents, Short Movie, etc...
		TEL / FAX	+81 (0)3 5842 7300 +81 (0)3 5842 7307
		E-MAIL URL	contents@cadcenter.co.jp http://www.cadcenter.co.jp/

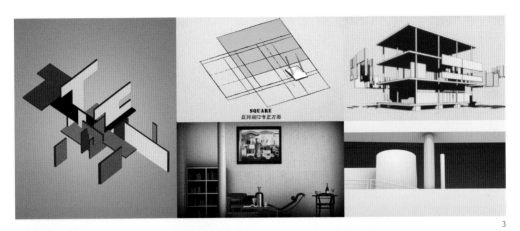

3

4

Founded in 1987. Focusing on the production of real estate promotional stills, motion graphics, VR data for city planning, and interactive content for exhibitions, they have in recent years been doing executing unique art-oriented motion graphics, making digital motion graphic records of scholarly and cultural resources, and animating paintings and engravings in 3-D.

008

權奇晶
KEE. J. CUON

弘益（ホンイック）芸術大学卒業後、KOREA TELECOM、LGにてマルチメディア映像デザインに携わる。その後、イギリスKINGSTON UNIVERSITY大学院でScreen design for film & TVコース修了。2004年空気株式会社に入社。MV、放送グラフィックスなど多様なスクリーンメディアのためのモーショングラフィックスを手がける。

1

2

1　Promotion DEMO Image
　　- EPSON OLED Display system
　　(EPSON, 2007)

2　Channel Package Design - ANIMAX
　　(©Animax Broadcast Japan Inc., 2007)

3　Promotion Image - MORISEIKI
　　(MORISEIKI, 2007)

4　Broadcasting Title Design - STARLEAGUE
　　(ongamenet ON*MEDIA Corp., 2007)

BELONG TO	空気株式会社 KOO-KI CO.,LTD.	CATEGORY	MV, CM, Short Movie, Animation
TOOLS	After Effects, Maya	TEL / FAX	+81 (0)92 874 2020 +81 (0)92 874 2010
		E-MAIL URL	fxfxf@koo-ki.co.jp http://www.koo-ki.co.jp

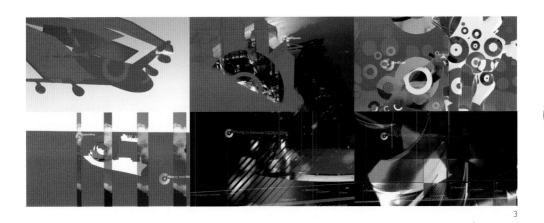

3

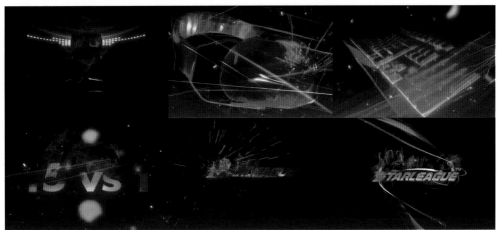

4

Born in Seoul, South Korea in 1972. After graduating from Hongik University, he
worked for KOREA TELECOM and LG as a creator in multimedia design field. After
he completed a MA course in Screen Design for Film and TV at Kingston University
in London, he joine KOO-KI in 2004 and focuses mainly on design works for all screen
media range, being involved in graphic design, motion graphics, promotion images,
broadcasting design and etc.

009

ダシ
DASI

2007年、映像ディレクターの岩井天志と浦野康介を中心に設立。CM、TV、MV、アニメーション、グラフィック、WEB と幅広い仕事を手がける。アートスペース Super Deluxe とのコラボレーションで映像コンテンツ、イベントの企画も行う。アート×遊び×仕事のスタンスで游泳中。

1

2

1	CM – 明治製菓「Sweet Life『かなわぬ恋篇』」 Meiji Seika, *Sweet Life~kanawanu koi hen.* (©MEIJI SEIKA KAISHA, LTD., 2007)	3	TV – NHK「きよしとこの夜」 *Kiyoshi to Kono Yoru* (©NHK, 2007)
2	TV – NHK 朝の連続テレビ小説「瞳」 *Hitomi* (©NHK, 2008)	4	Web – JTB「タビビト」*Tabibito* (©JTB Corp., 2007-2008)

TOOLS	After Effects, Final Cut, Flash	CATEGORY	CM, TV, MV, Short Movie, Animation, Web
		TEL / FAX	+81 (0)3 3478 3877 +81 (0)3 3478 3877
		E-MAIL	info@dasi.jp
		URL	http://www.dasi.jp

3

4

Dasi was founded in 2007, led by motion graphic directors Tenshi Iwai and Kosuke Urano. Their production work spans commercials, television, music videos, animation, graphics and the web. They are also involved in collaborating with the art space Super Deluxe on visual content and event planning. Their work ethic is art × play × work.

010

デラウエア
DELAWARE

音楽をデザインする、デザインを音楽するグループ。作品は、音楽、映像、文章、ウェブ、携帯電話、クロスステッチ、ライヴ・パフォーマンスなど多岐に渡る。自称アートゥーニスト。(アートゥーンは、アートとカートゥーンの合成語)。「あまり大きな声じゃ言えないけど、ぼくら人間だってことを誇りに思っているんだ」とも。

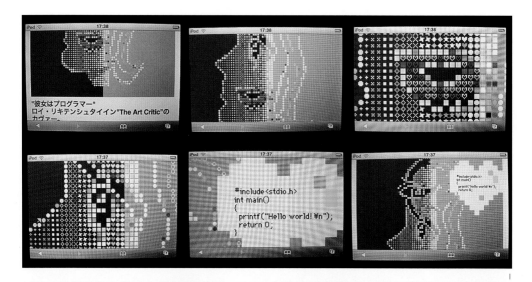

1

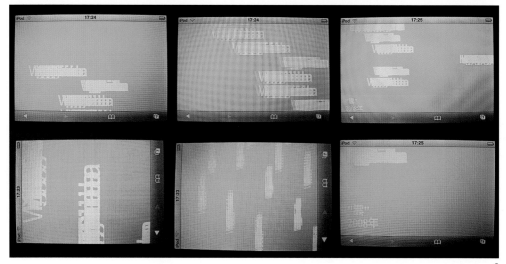

2

1 Web -「彼女はプログラマー」
   She's A Programmer. (2008)
   donow homepage for iPodtouch/iPhone
   http://www.do-now.jp/

2 Web -「雲」*Cloud* (2008)
   donow homepage for iPodtouch/iPhone

3 Web -「コピーのコピーのコピーのコピーのコ
   ピーのコピーのコピーのコピー ...」
   *Copy of copy of copy of copy of copy of copy
   of copy of copy of....* (2008)
   donow homepage for iPodtouch/iPhone

4 Mobile -「100万ドル」*1,000,000$* (2006)
   CTIA Wireless, NTTDoCoMo,
   at Las Vegas Convention Center

TOOLS	Director, GIF Builder, Color Cycle, QuickTime	CATEGORY	Exhibition, MV, Short Animation
		E-MAIL	mail@delaware.gr.jp
		URL	http://www.delaware.gr.jp/

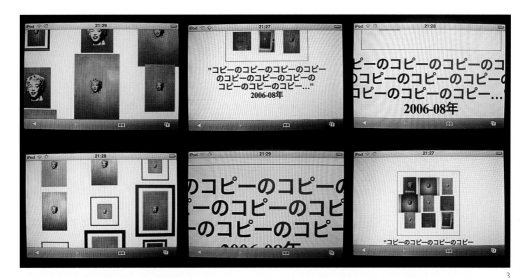

3

4

Delaware is a japanese super sonic group, designs music and musics design. Their works take on multiple forms such as recordings, visual installation, writing, web, mobile phone, poster, cross stitch, and live performance. They call themselves "Artoonist" (Artoon means art plus cartoon). And "Say it low, we are human being and we're proud".

011

ドロップ
DOLLOP

クリエイティブプロダクション WOW のディレクターユニット。コアメンバーはクリエイティブディ
レクター於保浩介、ディレクター真壁成尚、ビジュアルアートディレクター大内裕史。プロジェク
トによっては WOW のデザイナーを加え、多彩な表現スタイルを創り出す。CM、VI、WEB ムービー
などの企画からフィニッシュまでのトータルなディレクションを行う傍ら、メディアにとらわれな
い表現を目指し、実験的な映像制作にも積極的に挑戦している。

1

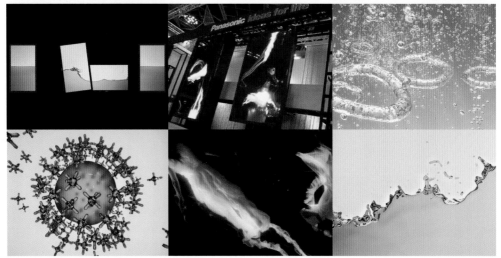

2

1	Original Works − *WOW10 project* (2007)	3	CM − *Sprite ZERO* (2007)
2	Exhibition Image − *Panasonic GEMINI* (2007)	4	Installation − *Pattern on Wallpaper* (2007)

BELONG TO	ワウ WOW	CATEGORY	CM, VI, Short Movie, Web Movie, Installation
TOOLS	3ds Max, After Effects, Final Cut, CINEMA 4D, Quartz Composer, Flash	TEL / FAX	+81 (0)3 5459 1100 +81 (0)3 5459 1101
		E-MAIL URL	info@w0w.co.jp http://www.dollop.jp http://www.w0w.co.jp

3

4

The directing unit of the creative production WOW. Core members are Kosuke Oho (Creative Director), Shigetaka Makabe (Director), and Hiroshi Ouchi (Visual Art Director). Other WOW designers also join them depending on the project. While handling all the phases of creating TV commercials, VIs and web movies, they work hard to produce experimental motion graphics without being shackled by any specific media.

012

イーズバック
EASEBACK

企画から映像制作、アートディレクション、プロデュースまでを手がけるクリエイティブチーム。国内外人気アーティストのCDジャケットやMV制作をキャリアの足がかりとしながら、ストリートの作法を進化させた変幻自在なアイデアでメディアにとらわれないアプローチを展開中。2007年の主な仕事はNTT DoCoMo携帯電話VP、矢沢永吉ツアー関連デザイン、HOUSE NATIONのCDジャケットデザインなど。

1

2

3

1　Product Promotion Movie –
　　NTT DoCoMo, 704i series DEBUT
　　(©NTT DoCoMo, 2007)

2　Store Promotion Movie – Levis, *PLAY HARD*
　　(©Levi Strauss Japan K.K., 2008)

3　MV – SeeK, *nande!? mono Panic!!!*
　　(©Starz, 2008)

4　MV – TUCKER, *SLASH-AND-D-Deck*
　　(©UNIVERSAL MUSIC K.K., 2007)

5　Steph Pockets, *Cant give up*
　　(©Victor Entertainment,Inc., 2007)

6　MV – Kaela Kimura, *Samantha*
　　(©Columbia Music Entertainment, Inc., 2007)

BELONG TO	イーズバック easeback	CATEGORY	MV, CM, Short Movie, Documentary, Animation
TOOLS	After Effects, Final Cut, Premiere	TEL / FAX	+81 (0)3 5452 2144 +81 (0)3 5452 2143
		E-MAIL URL	esbk@easeback.jp http://www.easeback.jp

4

5

6

7

7 MV - RUB-A-DUB MARKET, *SUNSHINE*
(©BMG JAPAN INC, 2007)

A creative team involved in everything from pre-production to photography, art direction and production. Starting from CD jackets and music video production of well-known artists at home and abroad, they are developing an approach to repel media co-option by using ever-changing ideas to further street methods. Main 2007 jobs were for NTT DoCoMo, Eikichi Yazawa, HOUSE NATION and Yokohama Reggae.

013

エレクロトニック
ELECROTNIK

グラフィックデザイン、CMなどで活躍していた中根ひろしと中根さやかが、映像製作会社で知り合い意気投合。2001年にデュオディレクターとしてELECTROTNIKを結成。CG、アニメーション、編集などの作業はすべて二人で行う。m-floの「prism」のPVを始め、これまで数多くのPVを手がける。また、エジンバラ国際映画祭やresfest等国内外のフィルムフェスティバルに出品し、高い評価を受けている。

1

2

1　MV – rize, *KAMI*
　(©Far Eastern Tribe Records, 2007)

2　MV – Kuchiroro, *Golden King*
　(©commmons, 2007)

3　CM – *sony walkman a*
　(©Sony Corporation, 2007)

4　*NIKE JAPAN+YOKOHAMA F・MARINOS*
　Director: ELECTROTNIK
　Production: TAIYO KIKAKU co.,ltd
　Advertising agency: Daiko Advertising Inc.

TOOLS	After Effects, DPS Reality, SOFTIMAGE XSI	CATEGORY	MV, CM, Movie, Animation
		TEL / FAX	+81 (0)3 3705 3046 +81 (0)3 3705 3047
		E-MAIL	info@elecrotnik.com
		URL	http://www.elecrotnik.com

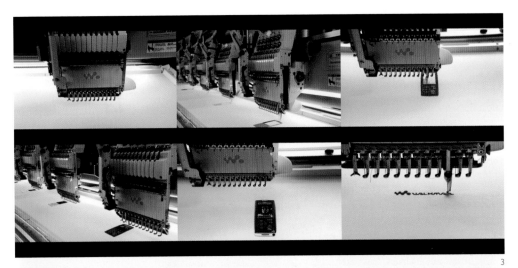

3

4

Hiroshi Nakane and Sayaka Nakane, who were both producing graphic design works and TV commercials, became acquainted at a motion graphic production company. In 2001, they formed Elecrotnik as dual directors. They handle every part of the production process by themselves, including CG, animation, and editing. They have made numerous music videos, such as M-flo's "Prism." They have received high praise for submitted works to film festivals such as Edinburgh International Film Festival and Resfest.

014

エンライトメント
ENLIGHTENMENT

ヒロ杉山、三嶋章義、鈴木シゲル、山口要からなるアーティストユニット。ファインアートの世界で作品を発表する一方、フリーペーパーやアートブックの出版、広告や雑誌、CDジャケットなどでも独創的なグラフィックを発表し続けている。さらにMVやVJなどの映像分野での評価も非常に高く、近年では平面だけでなく立体作品や空間演出も手がけ、ジャンルにとらわれない幅広い創作活動を展開している。

1

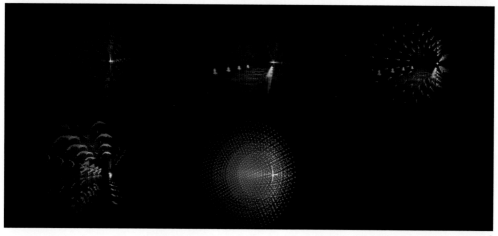

2

1   MV – Shinichi Osawa, *Star Guiter*
    (AVEX ENTERTAINMENT INC, 2007)

2   Original – *Fortune teller*
    (Enlightenment, 2007)

3   WEB Movie – *Laforet HARAJUKU* (2008)

4   Street Display Movie –
    What makes you smile ? Enlightenment ver.
    (TAICOCLUB, 2008)

| TOOLS | After Effects, Final Cut Pro | CATEGORY | MV, CM, Short Movie |

TOOLS   After Effects,
         Final Cut Pro

CATEGORY   MV, CM, Short Movie

TEL / FAX   +81 (0)3 3705 5470
          +81 (0)3 3705 5471

E-MAIL   hs@elm-art.com
URL   http://elm-art.com

3

4

Formed by Hiro Sugiyama, Akiyoshi Mishima, Shigeru Suzuki, and Kaname Yamaguchi.
They show at fine art exhibitions worldwide, also publishing art books and free paper, and
making creative graphic art for commercials, magazines, CD jackets, etc. Their reputation
in fields like promotional video and VJing is high, and recently they have gone beyond
2-dimensions, rendering space from 3-dimensional works as well.

015

ユーフラテス
EUPHRATES

慶應大学佐藤雅彦研究室の卒業生からなる、クリエイティブ・グループ。結成は 2005 年 12 月。映像、アニメーション、本、グラフィックデザインなど、メディアを問わず、考え方を重視した表現活動を行う。また、NHK 教育番組「ピタゴラスイッチ」では「ピタゴラ装置」をはじめとする番組の各コーナーのメインスタッフを務める。2007 年、ISSEY MIYAKE「A-POC INSIDE.」でニューヨーク ADC 金賞、メディア芸術祭アート部門優秀賞を受賞。

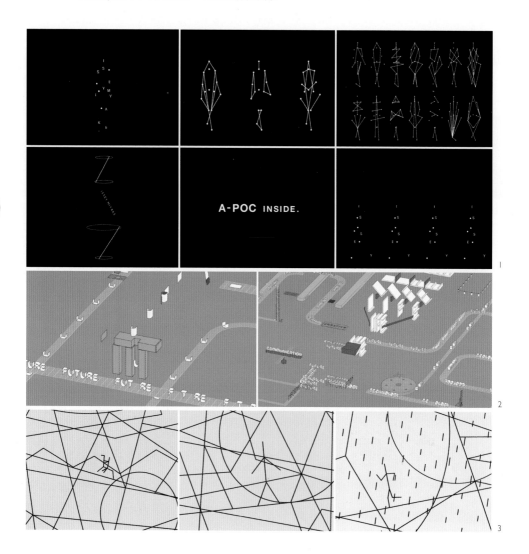

1

2

3

1　Short Movie – ISSEY MIYAKE, A-POC INSIDE.
(© ISSEY MIYAKE INC., 2007)
Created by Masahiko Sato + EUPHRATES
Creative Director: 佐藤雅彦 Masahiko Sato
Director: うえ田みお Mio Ueta
Music: 山本精一 Seiichi Yamamoto

2　Introduction Movie – Dai Nippon Printing, FACTORY
OF IDEAS (© Dai Nippon Printing Co., Ltd., 2006)
Created by Masahiko Sato + EUPHRATES + Masaya Ishikawa
Creative director: 佐藤雅彦 Masahiko Sato

Art Director: 石川将也 Masaya Ishikawa, 山本晃士
ロバート Kohji Robert Yamamoto, Director: 佐藤匡
Masashi Sato, Music: 服部隆之 Takayuki Hattori

3　MV – 真心ブラザーズ「きみとぼく」Magokoro Brothers,
Kimi to Boku (©Ki/oon Records Inc., 2007)
Created by EUPHRATES, Animator: うえ田みお Mio
Ueta, Creative Director: 佐藤雅彦 Masahiko Sato

4　NHK 教育番組 –「ピタゴラスイッチ」PythagoraSwitch
「10 本アニメ」10pon Anime

Animation + Planning: うえ田みお Mio Ueta, 貝塚智
子 Tomoko Kaizuka「ぼてじん」Botejin Animation +
Planning: うえ田みお Mio Ueta, 貝塚智子 Tomoko
Kaizuka「○と△のしゅうだん」○ to △ no Shuudan
Director: 佐藤匡 Masashi Sato,「もりのおく」Morino
Oku, Animator: うえ田みお Mio Ueta「オノマトペのう
た」Onomatope no Uta Animator: うえ田みお Mio Ueta
Planning + Production: ユーフラテス EUPHRATES
Superviser: 佐藤雅彦 Masahiko Sato, 内野真澄 Masumi
Uchino

TOOLS	After Effects, Final Cut, Vegas, LiveMotion, Maya, FrameThief	CATEGORY	TV Program, MV, Short Movie, Animation, Programming, Book, Graphic Design,
		TEL / FAX	+81 (0)3 6226 3113 +81 (0)3 6226 3112
		E-MAIL URL	euph@euphrates.co.jp http://euphrates.jp/

5 MV - 栗コーダーカルテット「おじいさんの11ヶ月」
Kuricorder Quartet, *Grandpapa's Eleven month*
(©2007 Geneon Entertainment INC.)
Created by EUPHRATES, Director: 佐藤匡 Masashi Sato

6 MV - 真心ブラザーズ「All I want to say to you」
Magokoro Brothers, *All I want to say to you*
(©Ki/oon Records Inc., 2007)
Created by EUPHRATES, Director：佐藤匡 Masashi Sato, Creative director：佐藤雅彦 Masahiko Sato

This group was founded by graduates of the Keio University Masahiko Sato Laboratory in December 2005. They create expressions based on new concepts in many different media, such as TV programs, music videos, and books. They work as the main staff for the NHK Educations "Pythagora Switch". New York ADC 86th Annual Awards Gold Prize and Japan Media Arts Festival Art Division Grand Prize for ISSEY MIYAKE "A-POC INSIDE.".

016

後藤章治
SHOJI GOTO

1973年生まれ。グラフィックデザイナー、画家、映像作家、ミュージシャン。様々なバンドのアルバムジャケット、MV、フライヤー、Tシャツなどの音楽に関わるアートワークを多数手がけ、また自身もミュージシャン。

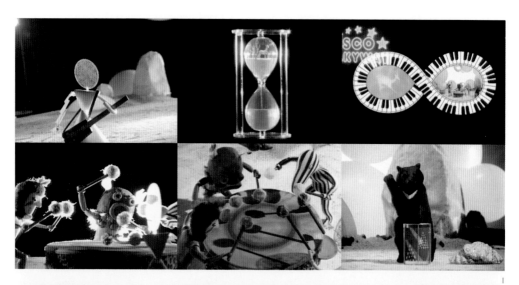

1

2

1 MV – OOIOO, *UMO* (℗felicity /
SHOCKCITY / THRILL JOCKEY, 2006)

2 MV – OOIOO, *EYƎ MIX* (℗felicity /
SHOCKCITY / THRILL JOCKEY, 2006)

3 MV – OOIOO, *UMA* (℗felicity /
SHOCKCITY / THRILL JOCKEY, 2006)

4 MV – OOIOO, *KILA KILA KILA*
(℗APE SOUNDS / THRILL JOCKEY, 2003)

BELONG TO	イーグルデザイン EAGLE DESIGN	CATEGORY	MV, CM, Short Movie, Animation
TOOLS	Photoshop, Illustrater, After Effects, Final Cut, SUPER 8	E-MAIL URL	info@shojigoto.com http://www.shojigoto. com

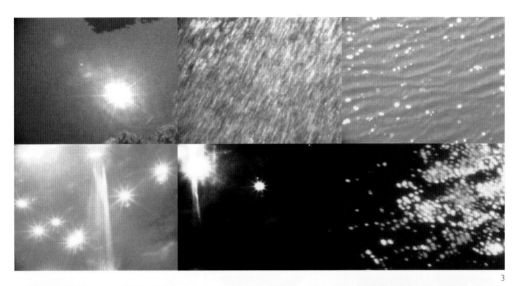

3

4

Born in 1973. A graphic designer, painter, motion graphic creator and musician.
Focusing mainly on the album covers, music videos, flyers and t-shirts of various bands,
he works on his own music as well.

017

グルーヴィジョンズ
GROOVISIONS

1993年以降、グラフィックやムービーを中心に、プロダクト、インテリア、ファッション、Webと様々な領域でデザインを行うデザイングループ。タレント「chappie.」の所属事務所。

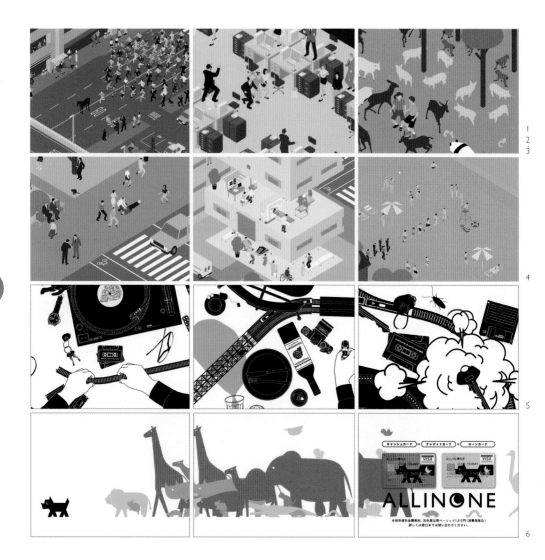

1
2
3

4

5

6

1	MV – HALFBY, *RODEO MACHINE* (SECOND ROYAL RECORDS, 2005)	4	MV – HALFBY, *Slip ON* (©TOY'S FACTORY Inc., 2006)	6	CM – *ALL IN ONE* (THE NISHI-NIPPON CITY BANK LTD., 2006) CD: Takao Ito / DR+CH+MO: groovisions
2	MV – HALFBY, *SCREW THE PLAN* (©TOY'S FACTORY Inc., 2006)	5	MV – Fantastic Plastic Machine feat.CLAZZIQUAI PROJECT, *don't you know?* (cutting edge, 2006)		M: Gakuji Matsuda (CUBISMO GRAFICO) PL: groovisions+Takao Ito+Toshiyuki Hidari C: Toshiyuki Hidari / PR: Kenichiro Ueda
3	MV – HALFBY, *HALFBEAT* (©TOY'S FACTORY Inc., 2006)				Production: groovisions+Dentsu kyusyu+T&E

TOOLS	After Effects, Final Cut, Photoshop, Illustrator	CATEGORY	MV, CM, Animation, Web
		TEL / FAX	+81 (0)3 5723 6558 +81 (0)3 5723 6356
		E-MAIL URL	grv@groovisions.com http://www.groovisions.com

7

G

8

9

7   Artwork – GRV2196 (Station navi)
    (Expo 2005 AICHI JAPAN) at EXPO 2005,
    AICHI, JAPAN, EXPO PLAZA, EXPO Vision
    CD: Spiral/Wacoal Art Center

8   MV – RIP SLYME, GOOD JOB!
    (©Warner Music Japan, 2005)

9   MV – RIP SLYME, SPEED KING
    (©Warner Music Japan, 2007)

A design group started in 1993 and focusing on things like graphic design and movies, while also involved in interiors, fashion, the web, and various other realms of design. Represents the artist "Chappie".

018

芳賀薫
KAORU HAGA

1973年東京生まれ。武蔵野美術大学映像学科卒業。PYRAMID FILM企画演出部を経て、2004年
「THE DIRECTORS GUILD」設立。CMを中心にショートムービーやMVも手がけるディレクター
として活動中。

1

2

I　CM - ソトコト「たばこ」
　Sotokoto, *Tobacco*
　(©KIRAKUSHA, Inc.)

2　CM - HELP ☆ MAN SHOW I「電球」*BULB*
　(©Hewlett-Packard Development Company,
　L.P., 2007)

3　CM - HELP ☆ MAN SHOW 2「コンパス」
　compass
　(©Hewlett-Packard Development Company,
　L.P., 2007)

4　MV - L'Arc~en~Ciel, *Hurry X'mas*
　(©Ki/oon Records Inc., 2007)

BELONG TO   ザ・ディレクターズ・ギルド
THE DIRECTORS
GUILD

CATEGORY   CM, MV, Short Movie

TEL / FAX   +81 (0)3 5712 5672
+81 (0)3 5712 5673

E-MAIL   tdg_info@d-guild.com
URL   http://www.d-guild.com/

3

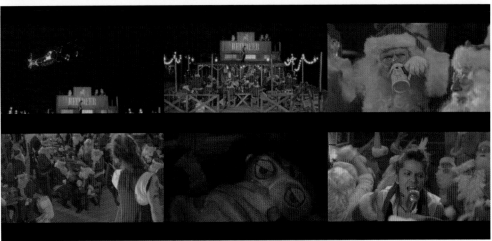

4

Born in Tokyo in 1973. graduated from department of motiongraphic art at Musashino
Art University. After working in production and direction at PYRAMID FILM, in 2004
he became one of the founders of THE DIRECTORS GUILD. Aside from commercials,
he also handles the direction of things like short movies and music videos.

019

半崎信朗
TOSHIAKI HANZAKI

1981年生まれ、2007年東京藝術大学大学院修了。自主制作作品「Birds（2005）」「Birthday（2007）」が多くのコンペティションでグランプリを受賞。それをきっかけにフリーランスの映像作家として活動を開始する。2007年より映像レーベル「Little Family Tree」に参加。主にアニメーションを用いたCM、OPなどを手がける。映像と音の関係を大切にするため、時に音楽も同時に制作する。

1

2

1	Original Work – *Birds* (Toshiaki Hanzaki, 2005)	3	OP –「田村亮一座」*Tamura Ryo Ichiza* (Yoshimoto Creative Agency Co., Ltd)
2	Original Work – *Birthday* (Toshiaki Hanzaki, 2007)	4	Opening Title –「エジソンの母」*Edison no Haha* (TBS, 2008)

TOOLS	After Effcts, Final Cut, SOFTIMAGE XSI, Photoshop, Illustrator	CATEGORY	MV, CM, Short Movie, Animation
		E-MAIL	mail@toshiaki-hanzaki.com
		URL	http://www.toshiaki-hanzaki.com

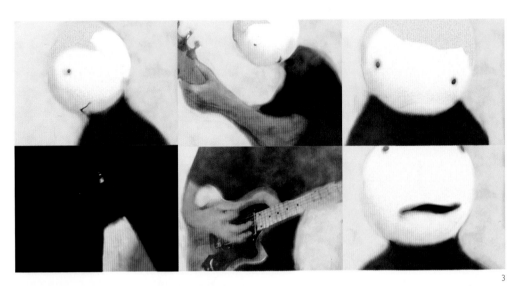

3

4

Born in 1981, graduated from Tokyo National University of Fine Arts and Music in 2007. Became freelance after winning prizes for "Birds" (2005) and "Birthday" (2007). In 2007 he joined "Little Family Tree". Mostly involved in commercials and opening sequences using animation. He creates the music at the same time as the images in order to respect the connection between the two.

020

針谷建二郎 / アダプター
KENJIRO HARIGAI / ADAPTER

1977年生まれ。アートディレクター、フィルムディレクター。2003年グラフィックチーム
ADAPTERを設立。グラフィックデザインをベースに企画や映像ディレクション、Webデザインな
ど幅広い仕事をこなす。2005年より平行してクリエイティブレーベル「Public/image.label」を主催。
2007年5月にクリエイティブスタジオ「ANSWR」を設立。今後も様々なプロジェクトを展開予定。

I	MV – m-flo loves BONNIE PINK, *Love Song* (rhythmzone, 2008)	3	MV – FREE TEMPO, *Dreaming* (SONY MUSIC PLAYERS, 2007)
2	MV – 椎名林檎 + 斉藤ネコ「茎」 Ringo Shiina + Neko Saito, *Kuki* (TOSHIBA EMI, 2007)	4	Short Movie – *BURTON ak Project* (BURTON, 2007)

BELONG TO	アンサー ANSWR	CATEGORY	MV, Short Movie, Animation
TOOLS	After Effects, Final Cut, Photoshop, Illustrator	TEL / FAX	+81 (0)50 8882 0088 +81 (0)3 5433 1138
		E-MAIL	info@answr.jp
		URL	http://www.adapter.jp

3

4

Born in 1977. Art director and film director. Founded the graphic team "ADAPTER" in 2003. With graphic design as a base, he is involved in planning, image direction, web design, and various other jobs. Since 2005 he has promoted the creative label "Public/image.label" on the side. He founded the creative studio "ANSWR" in May 2007. He plans to continue to expand the variety of his projects.

021

長谷川踏太
TOTA HASEGAWA

ロイヤルカレッジオブアート インタラクションデザイン科卒業。ソニー株式会社勤務を経て、英国
ロンドンに本拠地を置くクリエイティブ集団Tomatoに所属。インターネット広告やコーポレートア
イデンティティなどの分野でインタラクティブな作品を発表。そのほか、アーティストとしての作
品制作や文筆活動も行う。

1

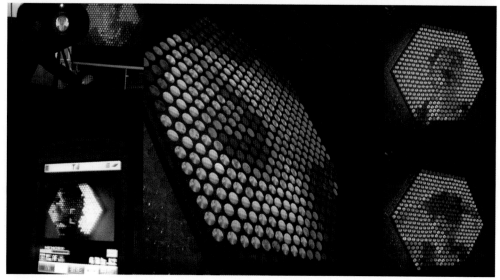

2

1　Interface&Contents Design –
　　NTT DoComo P703i μ
　　(©Panasonic Mobile Communications Co., Ltd.,
　　2007)

2　Instalation – *You Me Who*
　　(Kddi Corporation, 2005)

3　Interactive Video Installation –
　　Microsoft Office 2008 for Mac
　　AD: kashiwa sato(samurai)
　　(©Microsoft Corporation., 2008)

4　Window Display – *Aspesi shop (rome ,Milan)*
　　AD: dirk van dooren + tomato
　　(©Aspesi, 2007)

BELONG TO   トマト
                Tomato

CATEGORY   Motion Graphics, Art,
                    Interface Design

TEL / FAX   +44 (0)20 7253 5479
                    +44 (0)20 7253 5479

E-MAIL   tota@tomato.co.uk
URL   http://www.tomato.co.uk

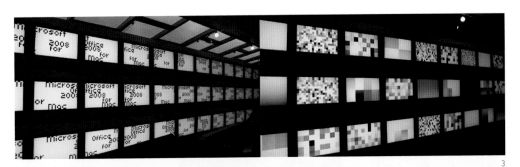

3

4

Graduate of the Royal College of Art in Interaction Design. He worked at Sony and then joined the creative group Tomato, which is based in London. He produces interactive works in fields like internet advertising and corporate identity. He is also active as an artist, producing writing and works of art etc.

022

橋本ダイスケ
DAISUKE HASHIMOTO

1977年生まれ。2005年クリエイティブプロダクションP.I.C.S.入社。グラフィック・イラストレーション・アニメーション・ディレクションをトータルに行う映像作家／アニメーション作家。近年はCM・MV・On Air Promotionなどの企画・演出、CGアニメーションを中心に活動中。「flowery」で平成17年度（第9回）文化庁メディア芸術祭 アニメーション部門 優秀賞受賞。

1

2

	Image Movie – CHRISTIAN BAUER, *Tree of Life* (©UMEX Co., 2007) Director+Animation: 橋本ダイスケ Daisuke Hashimoto, Camera: 西田香織 Kaori Nishida, Styring: 森久美子 Kumiko Mori, HM: 新宮利彦 Toshihiko Shingu, Music: 佐々木亨 Toru Sasaki, Producer: 清水忠 Tadashi Shimizu, Production by P.I.C.S.
2	CM – マードゥレクス Ex:beaute「接近する女篇」 madre:X Ex:beaute, *Sekkinsuru Onna* (2007) Director+Animation: 橋本ダイスケ Daisuke Hashimoto, Director: 遠崎寿義 Toshio Touzaki, Camera: 山中隆宏 Takahieo Yamanaka Music: 佐々木亨 Toru Sasaki, Producer: 寺井弘典 Hironori Terai, 清水忠 Tadashi Shimizu, Production by P.I.C.S.
3	Image Movie – PIONEER「楽ナビ ART CAR COLLECTION Opening」*Raku Navi ART CAR COLLECTION Opening* (©Pioneer, 2007) Director+Animation: 橋本ダイスケ Daisuke Hashimoto Music: 佐々木亨 Toru Sasaki, Producer: 清水忠 Tadashi Shimizu, Production by P.I.C.S.

BELONG TO	**P.I.C.S.**
TOOLS	After Effects, Photoshop, Illustrator, **CINEMA 4D**

CATEGORY	**CM, OAP, MV**
TEL / FAX	**+81 (0)3 5785 1780** **+81 (0)3 5785 1784**
E-MAIL	**post@picsco.net**
URL	**http://www.picsco.net**

3

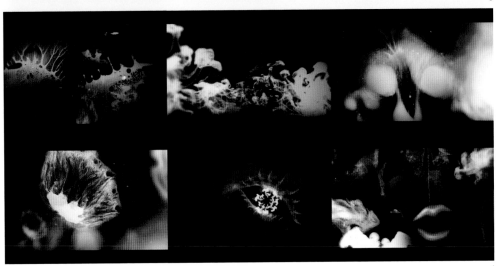

4

4 MV- 椎名林檎×斎藤ネコ『平成風俗大吟醸』DVD Video「ハツコイ媚女」Ringo Shena × Neko Saito, HEISEI FUZOKU DAIGINJO:DVD VIDEO, *Hatsukoi Shoujo* (©EMI Music Japan Inc., 2007)
Director+Animation: 橋本ダイスケ Daisuke Hashimoto, Producer: 松居秀之 Hideyuki Matsui, Production by P.I.C.S.

Born in 1977. He has joined the creative production firm P.I.C.S. in 2005. He is involved in computer graphic, illustration, animation and planning and direction of TV commercials, music videos and on-air promotions. He is a director and animation auteur who handles everything; graphics, illustration, animation and direction. His original motion graphic work "flowery" won an Excellence Award in the Animation Division of the 2005 Japan Media Arts Festival.

023

ハートボム
HEART BOMB

他社比社所属の映像ディレクター集団。MV、TVCM、ビデオインスタレーションを手がけるほか、QUICK TIMERS名義で定点観測映像を研究し、コミックアニメーション、CG、VIDEOCAMフィードバック、決定的瞬間映像、オシロスコープ波形をMIXする独自のVJスタイルが話題となり、ビッグフェスティバルにも多数出演。デコレーションチーム宇宙警備隊と共にLEDを用いた大規模な照明＆VJセットも考案し、さらには、音、風、重力などのあらゆる物理量を電気信号に変えてのインタラクティブなVJ、映像、LED演出も計画中。

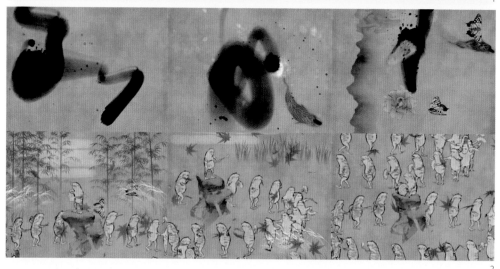

1

2

1	MV – WRENCH, *feel more* (Cutting Edge, Third culture, 2007)	3	MV – Shijinsandaimeuotakehamadashigeo, *Aishiteru* (EMI Music Japan Inc., 2007)
2	MV – Shinichi OSawa, *Last Days* (avex entertainment, TEAM☆LAB, Suzuki Yohei, 2007)	4	VJ – *CONNECT07 Chochin LEDJ* (Heineken Music, BNM, Uchu Keibitai, 2007)

BELONG TO	**イセネエヒヒネエ** iseneehihinee	CATEGORY	MV, CM, Short Movie, Animation, VJ
TOOLS	After Effects, Final Cut, Premiere	E-MAIL URL	info@heartbomb.jp http://heartbomb.jp/

3

4

A group of Iseneehihinee motion graphic directors. They make music videos, commercials and video installations, and research fixed-point observation footage (as "Quick Timers"). They mix comic animation, CG, videocam feedback, "moment of truth" footage and oscilloscope waveforms, the original style gets into a news and they performed at many big festivals. With the decoration team "Uchu Keibitai", they devised a massive illumination and VJ set. In their interactive VJing they convert every physical quantity (ie: sound, wind, gravity), into electrical signals; they also conceive the footage and LEDs.

024

東弘明
HIROAKI HIGASHI

1980年鳥取生まれ。芸短大卒業後、渡米。3DCGを習得。チーフデザイナーとしてコナミに在籍した後フリーランスとなる。PV、CMのCGディレクションを経て、ディレクターへ。企画/演出、CG、編集、合成をトータルに行う。

1

2

1	MV – APOGEE, 「アヒル」 Ahiru (Victor Entertainment, 2007)	3	MV – Crystal Kay, *dream world* (EPIC Records Japan, 2007)
2	MV – 元ちとせ Hajime Chitose, 「ミヨリの森」 Miyori no Mori (EPIC Records Japan, 2007)	4	MV – PE'Z, *NA!NA!NA!* (ROADRUNNER JAPAN, 2005)

BELONG TO	STOIC SENSE PRODUCT	CATEGORY	MV, CM
TOOLS	Maya, After Effects, Final Cut	TEL / FAX	+81 (0)3 3419 1319 +81 (0)3 3419 1319
		E-MAIL	info@stoicsenseproduct.com
		URL	http://www.stoicsenseproduct.com

3

4

Born in Tottori Prefecture in 1980. After graduating from Kansai Professional College of Art and Design, he went to the United States where he learned 3-D CG. After a stint as a chief designer at Konami, he became freelance. He was in charge of CG for promotional videos and Commercial, become a director. He produces and directs the entire process from computer graphics through editing and completion.

025

細野ひで晃
HIDEAKI HOSONO

1973年、西ドイツデュッセルドルフ生まれ。ロサンゼルス・アートセンターカレッジ卒業。1997年に帰国し、映画「ア・ルースボーイ」（松竹）を演出。電通テックを経て、2004年「THE DIRECTORS GUILD」を設立。2006年、DAYTORA ENTERTAINMENT設立。TV-CMなどの映像分野以外にも「日本を広告する」をテーマに「おばハニー」（http://www.obahoney.com/）プロジェクトを展開中。

1

2

1	CM – Coca-Cola Zero – BBQ (©Coca-Cola (Japan) Company, Limited., 2007)	3	CM – BOSS 贅沢微糖「贅沢タクシー」 BOSS ZEITAKU BITOH, *ZEITAKU TAXI* (©Suntory Limited., 2008)
2	CM – 新しい世界 *A NEW WORLD* (©DIC Corporation, 2007)	4	TV –「月曜映画オープニングタイトル」カントくん Nichiyou Eiga Opening Movie, *Kanto-kun* (©Nippon Television Network Corporation., 2008)

BELONG TO ザ・ディレクターズ・ギルド CATEGORY CM, MV, Short Movie
      THE DIRECTORS
      GUILD

            TEL / FAX +81 (0)3 5712 5672
                  +81 (0)3 5712 5673

            E-MAIL   tdg_info@d-guild.com
            URL   http://www.d-guild.com/

3

4

Born in Dusseldorf in 1973. Graduated from the Los Angeles Art Center College. When he came to Japan in 1997, he directed the Shochiku movie "A Loose Boy".
After working at Dentsu Tec, in 2004 he became one of the founders of THE DIRECTORS GUILD. In 2006 he founded DAYTORA ENTERTAINMENT. Aside from working in areas like the images for TV commercials, he in the middle of developing a project called "Oba Honey" with the theme of "publicizing Japan."

026

ホッチカズヒロ
HOTCHI KAZUHIRO

1979年生まれ。多摩美術大学在学中にアニメ制作を始める。2000年NHKデジタルスタジオに作品が取り上げられたのを期に作家として活動を始め、東京芸術大学大学院を経て、2005年にみんなのうた「空へ」でデビュー。HPでアニメ公開中。

1

2

1	Animation – *DOUDOU* (©Hotchi Kazuhiro, 2002)	3	TV – 岡本知高 Tomotaka Okamoto, 空へ *Sora he* (NHKみんなのうた, ©NHK / Hotchi Kazuhiro, 2005)
2	Animation – アニマ *Anima* (©Hotchi Kazuhiro, 2005)	4	MV – アン・サリー Ann Sally, のびろのびろだ いすきな木 *Nobiro Nobiro Daisukina Ki* (NHKみんなのうた, ©NHK / Hotchi Kazuhiro, 2007)

TOOLS   After Effects,
               Photoshop,
               Illustrator,
               Premiere

CATEGORY   MV, CM, Animation,
               Illustration, Design,
               Picture Book

E-MAIL   hotchi@directions.jp
URL   http://hotchi.main.jp/

3

4

Born in 1979. Began creating animation while still a student at Tama Art University. His career as a creator essentially began in 2000 when his work was picked up by NHK Digital Stadium. He went to graduate school at the Tokyo National University of Fine Arts and Music and debuted in 2005 on Minna No Uta with "Sora E". His animation can be seen on his website.

027

市村幸卯子
YUKO ICHIMURA

神奈川県横浜市生まれ。2000年ロンドン大学ゴールドスミスカレッジ現代美術科卒業。同年よりロンドンでアニメーターとして活動開始。在英11年を経て2005年帰国、(株) ピラミッドフィルム入社。アートディレクションのできる映像ディレクターとして、東京をベースに国内外のクライアントワークを手がける。

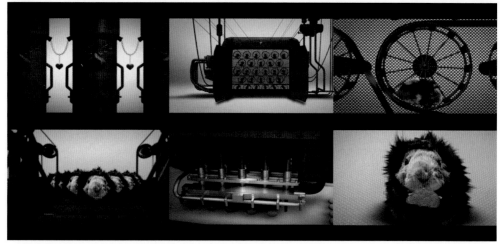

1　MV – JONTE「道の先」Michi no Saki
　　(©avex entertainment Inc., 2008)

4　MV – 椎名林檎×斉藤ネコ
　　Ringo Shiina × Neko Saito「迷彩」Meisai
　　(©EMI Music Japan Inc., 2007)

3　CM – ピンキー「モンキーいっぱい篇」
　　Pinky, Monkey Ippai
　　(©NaN Frente International Co.,Ltd., 2008)

2　TV –「ZAMURAI TV 弐」ZAMURAI TV 2
　　(©SPACE SHOWER NETWORK, 2007)

BELONG TO	ピラミッドフィルム PYRAMID FILM INC.	CATEGORY	CM, MV, Short Movie, DVD, Manga
TOOLS	Illustrator, Photoshop, After Effects, Final Cut, Flash & Hand	TEL	+81 (0)3 3434 0840
		E-MAIL	yuko@pyramidfilm.co.jp
		URL	http://www.pyramidfilm.co.jp/

3

4

Born in Yokohama City, Kanagawa Prefecture. Graduated with a BA in Fine Arts from Goldsmiths College, London. That same year, she commenced activities in London as an animator. After living in England for 11 years, she returned to Japan and started working at PYRAMID FILM INC. Making Tokyo her base, she works with her clients both domestically and abroad as a motion graphic director who can also do art direction.

028

稲葉まり
MARI INABA

多摩美術大学卒業。クリエイティブユニット生意気を経て独立。グラフィックデザイン、アニメーション制作を中心に活動中。ドローイングやコマ撮りのアニメを用いてYUKI「66db」MV制作や、UA「黄金の緑」MVに参加。2007年「キロロあやののあそびうた」にてアートディレクション、アニメーション制作を行う。2008年Rie fu「Home」MVディレクション。WEB絵本「どんぴとチャピロ 宇宙の旅へ」が公開中。金谷裕子氏と制作したアニメ作品は2007年BECK来日公演ライブ映像として使用された。

1

2

1　Stage – 星の行方 *Hoshi no Yukue* (2008)
　Director: Yasunori Ikunishi
　Dance: Ayano Teramoto
　Music: Gutevolk, Takashi Ueno(Tenniscoats)
　Visuals: Yasunori Kakegawa
　Animation: Mari Inaba, Yasuko Seki
　Organizer: SuperDeluxe
　Photography: top&right, Ooki Jingu
　left: HATSUE

2　DVD – キロロあやののあそびうた
　kiroro Ayano no Asobi Uta
　(©2007 Victor Entertainment, Inc., 2007)
　Director: Go Ikeda / Graphical director&
　Art work: Yasuko Ishimori, Mari Inaba /
　Title back design&animation: Mari Inaba
　Visual coordinator: Ayumi Hara

3　MV – Rie fu, *Home*
　(©Palm Beach Inc., 2008)
　Director: Mari Inaba, Yuko Kanatani
　Producer: Koji Takayama

4　Online picture book –
　どんぴとチャピロ 宇宙の旅へ
　(©SoftBank Creative Corp., 2006)
　Donpi to Chapiro Uchu no Tabie
　Picture, story: Mari Inaba
　Music& narration: Saya sauce(Tenniscoats)

BELONG TO	After Effects, Final Cut, Photoshop, Illustrator, Flash	CATEGORY	Animation, MV, Graphic Design, Illustration, Short Movie, Movie, CM
		E-MAIL	info_mariinaba@yahoo.co.jp

3

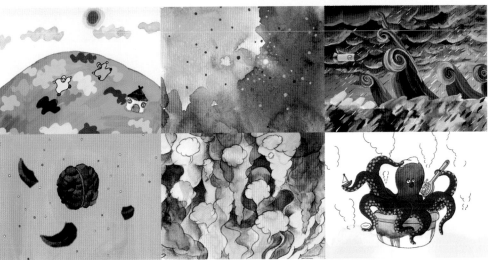

4

Graduate of Tama Art University, member of Namaiki, then freelance. Does mostly
graphic design and animation. Using drawing, stop-motion animation and other methods,
makes videos like Yuki's "66db" and was involved in UA's "Golden Green". "Kiroro Ayano
no Asobi Uta" art director and animator in 2007. Directed Rei Fu's "Home" in 2008. Her
picture book "Donpi to Chapiro Uchu no Tabi e" is online. With Yuko Kanatani made
animation for Beck's 2007 Japan shows.

029

稲本真帆
MAHO INAMOTO

エディター。1976年生まれ。日本大学芸術学部放送学科卒業後、1999年ROBOT入社。ノンリニア編集のノウハウを学び、TV-CM「KIRIN淡麗」シリーズ、映画「ファンタスティポ」（05年）などCMを中心に、映画、PV、Webムービー、ドキュメンタリーなど幅広いジャンルの編集を手がける。ナレーターとしても活躍中。

1　CM – Panasonic, *VIERA - Feel with your body.* (Panasonic (CIS) OY., 2007)
Director: 守本亨 Toru Morimoto
Producer: 髙橋良昌 Yoshimasa Takahashi
Production: ROBOT

2　CM – Microsoft「Xbox 360 – do!do!do! テニス篇」*Xbox 360 "do!do!do! tennis"* (Microsoft Co., Ltd., 2006)
Director: 守本亨 Toru Morimoto
Producer: 天野貴功 Takanori Amano
Production: ROBOT

BELONG TO	ロボット ROBOT	CATEGORY	CM, MV, Movie, Web Movie, VP
TOOLS	Avid Media Composer, Adrenaline, Final cut, After Effects, Illustrator, Photoshop	TEL / FAX	+81 (0)3 3760 1064 +81 (0)3 3760 1347
		E-MAIL URL	maho@robot.co.jp http://www.robot.co.jp

2

Editor, born in 1976. After graduating in broadcasting from Nihon University, she started working at ROBOT in 1999. She learned the know-how of nonlinear editing and has editing a wide variety of material including the TV commercial series "Kirin Tanrei" and the movie "Fantastipo" (2005), focusing on commercials, movies, promotional videos, web movies and documentaries. She is also a narrator.

030

井上卓
TAKU INOUE

1975年生まれ。東京工芸大学芸術学部卒業。1998年MTV Station-IDコンテスト受賞をきっかけ
に、MTV JAPAN入社。クリエイティブプロダクションP.I.C.S.を経て現在フリーランス。Promax &
BDA ゴールド受賞、2005年 OTTAWA international animation festival（カナダ）／ 2006年 annecy
international animation festival（フランス）作品上映など、海外での作品上映・受賞多数。

1

2

1	CM - SOFT99 コーポレーション ぬりぬりガラコ「ガラコ ロケット篇」SOFT99 Corporation Nuri Nuri Garaco, *Garaco "Rocket"*	2	Package Opening - *MTV SCREEN*	4	CM - 関西電力 環境広告「ツバル篇」THE KANSAI ELECTRIC POWER CO., INC. Environmental Advertising, *Tuvalu*

1 CM - SOFT99 コーポレーション ぬりぬりガラコ「ガ
ラコ ロケット篇」SOFT99 Corporation Nuri Nuri
Garaco, *Garaco "Rocket"*
Director: 井上卓 Taku Inoue, Camera: 吉田好伸 Yoshinobu
Yoshida, Light: 一明圭三 Keizo ichimei, CG: JINNI'S, A&P:
電通関西 + サン・アド DENTSU INC. Kansai + SUN-AD
COMPANY LIMITED (©SOFT99 Corporation, 2007)

2 Package Opening - *MTV SCREEN*
Director: 井上卓Taku Inoue, Camera: 深谷敦彦
Atsuhiko Fukatani, CG: JINNI'S, Music: 益田泰地 Taichi
Masuda (©MTV NETWORKS JAPAN, 2007)

3 MV - Clownfish「君とのサンデイ」*KIMI TONO SUNDAY*
Director+Character Design: 井上卓 Taku Inoue, CG:
JINNI'S, Producer: 上里滋 Shigeru Agari, Production
by P.I.C.S. (©R and C Ltd., 2007)

4 CM - 関西電力 環境広告「ツバル篇」THE KANSAI
ELECTRIC POWER CO., INC. Environmental Advertising,
Tuvalu
Director: 井上卓 Taku Inoue, CG: JINNI'S, A: 電通関
西 DENTSU INC. Kansai (©THE KANSAI ELECTRIC
POWER CO., INC., 2008)

BELONG TO	P.I.C.S.management	CATEGORY	Live Action, Illustration, Animation
TOOLS	Power Mac G4, Photoshop, After Effects	TEL / FAX	+81 (0)3 5785 1780 +81 (0)3 5785 1784
	(The material production is mainly used.)	E-MAIL URL	post.mg@picsco.net http://www.picsco.net

3

4

5

5　Web Site Movie - JUN 50th Anniversary
　Director+Animation+SE: 井上卓 Taku Inoue
　(©JUN CO.,LTD., 2007)

Born in 1975. Graduated from the Tokyo Polytechnic University Faculty of Arts. Inoue started working at MTV Japan after winning an award in the 1998 MTV Station ID Contest. After MTV, he worked for the creative production firm P.I.C.S. and is now freelance. He has had many screenings and won many awards around the world including the gold award at Promax & BDA , screenings at the 2005 OTTAWA International Animation Festival and the 2006 Annecy International Animation Festival.

031

伊藤有壱
YUICHI ITO

東京藝術大学美術学部デザイン科卒。1998年アイトゥーン設立、同代表。クレイを中心に様々な技法を駆使し、TV-CM、番組、MV、劇場映画などで活躍するアニメーションディレクター。代表作「ニャッキ!」（NHK教育）のほか、宇多田ヒカルや平井堅のMV、劇場発信型ショートアニメーション「NORABBITS' MINUTES（ノラビッツ・ミニッツ）」なども手がける。2008年度より東京藝術大学大学院映像研究科アニメーション専攻の教授に就任。

1

2

1 Animation - *NORABBITS' MINUTES Episode1~5* (©I.TOON/SHOCHIKU)
Production: Shochiku Co.,Ltd., Director, Script & Character Design:Yuichi Ito, Model Animator: Fumi Inoue, Animation:I.TOON, Music Producer: Naoto Sekiguchi, Composition Arrangement & Musical Performance: Masae Abe, Sound Producer: Masaki Matsubara

2 CM - WAKASA SEIKATU, *Blueberry Eye New Dance version* (WAKASA SEIKATU Co.,Ltd.,2007) AD Agency: AD DENTSU OSAKA INC.,

Production: Hit Hot Headers INC., Character Design & Director: Yuichi Ito, CG:POLYGON PICTURES INC., Music: Rei Sumii (free as a bird,inc.)

3 MV - Park Yong Ha, *Eien* (©2007 PONY CANYON INC.) Character Design+Director: Yuichi Ito Model Animator: Fumi Inoue Art Director: Yuta Ujiie Digital Composite: Kouske Nishimoto

4 CM - Pinky, *Monkey Ippai Version* (Frente International Co.,Ltd.) Agency: BRANCO inc.+Shinto Tsushin Co.,Ltd. Production: PYRAMID FILM INC. Animation Director: Yuichi Ito CG: POLYGON PICTURES INC.

BELONG TO	アイトゥーン	CATEGORY	Animation, CM, MV,
	I.Toon Ltd.		Character Design, Planning,
			Set Design, Logo Design,
TOOLS	After Effects,		Station ID
	Final Cut,		
	Illustrator,	TEL / FAX	+81 (0)45 222 6255
	Photoshop,		+81 (0)45 662 9736
	CLAYTOWN,		
	LunchBox	E-MAIL	itoon@mu2.so-net.ne.jp
		URL	http://www.i-toon.org

3

4

Graduated from the Tokyo National University of Fine Arts and Music ("Geidai"), General Design Course. Established I. Toon Ltd. in 1998. Focuses on clay animation and directs TV programs, commercials, music videos and theaterfilms. Made "Knyack!" for NHK Educational TV, also involved in Hikaru Utada and Ken Hirai music videos, and the short animation film "Norabbits' Minutes" (originally for the theatre). In 2008, became a professor in a postgraduate animation department of Geidai.

032

岩元正幸
MASAYUKI IWAMOTO

1999年初頭に映像制作チーム100LDK結成。クラブを中心にVJ活動を開始。Paul Van Dyk、Deep Dish、John Digweed など海外からのトップDJ来日時にVJを担当。sonarsound tokyo や metamorphose などに出演。サザンオールスターズやSOUL'd OUT など国内のアーティストのコンサート映像のディレクションも行っている。

I

2

I	Live - SOUL'd OUT Single Collection Tour (2007)	3	VP - docomo 905i, 705i (2007)
2	MV - THOROUGHBLEND, haruka (2007)	4	VJ - VJ works (2006)

BELONG TO	バニラインク / 100 エルディーケー vanilla inc. / 100LDK	CATEGORY	AD, MV, VJ, Animation
		TEL / FAX	+81 (0)3 5730 8445 +81 (0)3 5730 8446
TOOLS	After Effects, Final Cut	E-MAIL URL	iwamoto@vanillainc.com http://www.vanillainc.com

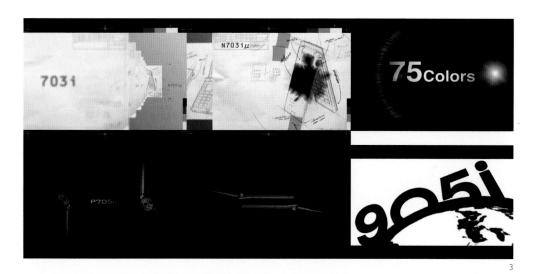

3

4

Set up his first motion graphic creation team "100LDK" in 1999. Began VJing, mostly in clubs. In charge of VJing for top DJ's from abroad like Paul Van Dyk, Deep Dish and John Digweed. Appeared at Sonarsound Tokyo, Metamorphose, others. Also involved in motion graphic direction for the concerts of domestic bands like Southern All Stars and Soul'd Out.

033

ジュウリョク
JURYOKU

2004年、WOW所属デザイナー中路琢磨、水野祐佑、工藤薫により結成した、クリエイティブクリエイティブユニット。2004年制作「Poetry of Suburbs」でRESFEST 2005 World Tourにノミネート。graf、Yoshio Kuboとのコラボレーションによる作品「fit-ment」ではインターフェイスに反応し、レイアウトが無限に変化するリアルタイムモーショングラフィックス作品を制作。

1

2

| 1 | Web Site – SHARP AQUOS VISION | 3 | Exhibition Image – HITACHI WOOO, Dream on |
| 2 | TVCM – 「National パルックプレミア L」 PALOOK PREMIERE L | 4 | Graphic Work – WOW10 森脇大輔 Daisuke Moriwaki + JURYOKU, HOMEOSTASIS |

BELONG TO	ワウ WOW	CATEGORY	CM, VI, Short Movie, Web Movie, Installation
TOOLS	After Effects, CINEMA 4D, Illustrator, Photoshop	TEL / FAX	+81 (0)3 5459 1100 +81 (0)3 5459 1101
		E-MAIL URL	info@w0w.co.jp http://www.w0w.co.jp/ juryoku http://www.w0w.co.jp

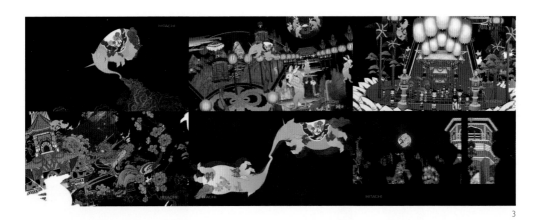

3

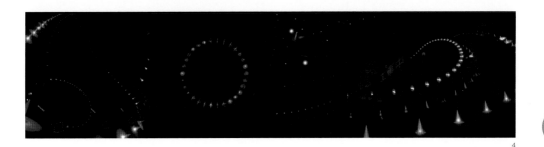

4

In 2004 WOW designers Takuma Nakaji, Yusuke Mizuno and Kaoru Kudo founded "JURYOKU". "Poetry of Suburbs" was nominated for the RESFEST 2005 World Tour. In their collaboration "fit-ment" with graf and Yoshio Kubo, there is interface response, and they make real time motion graphic works whose layouts limitlessly transform.

034

ケープラスミー
K+ME

Jeremy（College of Visual Communication, France 卒業）と Kaoru（London College of Communication, U.K. 卒業）によるクリエイティブユニット。2005年ロンドンにて結成、"Organic"をコンセプトに身近な素材を使った作品制作を心がけている。2006年11月に東京に移り、本格的な共同作業を開始。映像のほか、イラストレーション、グラフィック、エディトリアルデザインを手がける。

1

2

| 1 | Short movie – *La kaltso* (2005) | 3 | Event movie – 「ハダギネ」
Lowrys Farm (2007) |
| 2 | Original Work – *Man Standing Up* (2006) | 4 | MV – Leonard de Leonard, *Screaming Dance*
(©Ekleroshock records, 2007) |

TOOLS	After Effects, Final Cut	CATEGORY	MV, CM, Short Movie, Animation
		TEL	+81 (0)3 6420 3102
		E-MAIL	hello@kplusme.com
		URL	http://www.kplusme.com

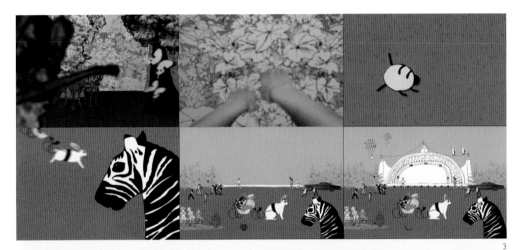

3

4

Founded in London in 2005 by Jeremy, graduate of the College of Visual Communication in France, and Kaoru of the London College of Communication. Work based on the organic concept of using materials close at hand. Moved operations to Tokyo in November 2006 and began their collaboration in earnest. Aside from motion graphics, also involved in illustration, graphic design and editorial design.

035

喜田夏記
NATSUKI KIDA

1976年生まれ。東京藝術大学美術学部デザイン科大学院修了。在学中からMV・TV-CM等で様々な映像作品を制作。映像ディレクションのほか、作画から美術制作、アニメーション、編集までをトータルに行う。CDジャケット、VOGUE、流行通信などのアートディレクション、niDoの浴衣、テキスタイルデザインも手がける。エジンバラ国際映画祭・Vila do Conde（ポルトガル映画祭）・Anifest作品招待、文化庁メディア芸術祭審査員推薦作品受賞、ロンドン／ヴィクトリア＆アルバート美術館企画展にて作品上映など。現在フリーのディレクターとして活動中。

1

2

1 MV – 中島美嘉「永遠の詩」Mika Nakashima, *Eien no Uta* (©Sony Music Associated Records Inc., 2007)
Director+Art+Animation : 喜田夏記 Natsuki Kida,
Animation: 清水修 Osamu Shimizu, 久保コレオ Koreo Kubo, 大野幹 Motoki Ohno, Art: 池亀沙織 Saori Ikekame, Camera: 小林基己 Motoki Kobayashi, Light: 野村泰寛 Yasuhiro Nomura, Producer: 小浜元 Hajime Kohama, Production by P.I.C.S.

2 MV – 倖田來未 Kumi Koda, *Wonderland* (©avex entertainment inc., 2008)
Director+Art+Animation : 喜田夏記 Natsuki Kida,
Animation: 喜田直哉 Naoya Kida, 清水修 Osamu Shimizu, 大野幹 Motoki Ohno, Art: 池亀沙織 Saori Ikekame, Camera: 小川ミキ Miki Ogawa, Light: 野村泰寛 Yasuhiro Nomura, Producer: 小浜元 Hajime Kohama, Production by P.I.C.S.

3 MV – 勝手にしやがれ + 中島美嘉 Mika Nakashima, *YOU'D BE SO NICE TO COME HOME TO* (©Epic Records Inc., 2007)
Director+Art: 喜田夏記 Natsuki Kida,
Camera: 小川ミキ Miki Ogawa, Light: 野村泰寛 Yasuhiro Nomura, Producer: 小浜元 Hajime Kohama, Production by P.I.C.S.

BELONG TO	P.I.C.S.management	CATEGORY	Live Action, Animation, Art Direction
TOOLS	Power Mac G5 Quad, Photoshop, After Effects, Final Cut Pro	TEL / FAX	+81 (0)3 5785 1780 +81 (0)3 5785 1784
		E-MAIL	post.mg@picsco.net
		URL	http://www.picsco.net

3

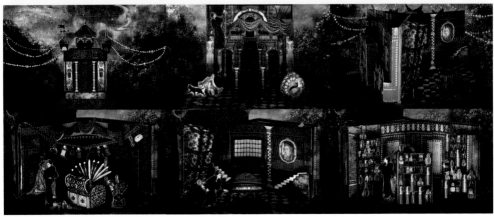

4

Art Center College Library
1700 Lida St.
Pasadena, CA 91103

4　Web Movie - 資 生 堂 MAJOLICA MAJORCA /
chapter16 (©Shiseido Co.,Ltd., 2007)
Director+Art+Animation : 喜田夏記 Natsuki Kida,
Pop Up Design: 喜田夏記 Natsuki Kida, 喜田直哉
Naoya Kida, Animation: 清 水 修 Osamu Shimizu,
Art: 池亀沙織 Saori Ikekame,
Music・SE: 木下習子 Shuko Kinoshita,
A&P: Shiseido Co.,Ltd. + BBmedia Inc.

Born in 1976. Graduate Design Degree from the Tokyo National University
of Fine Arts and Music. Work includes commercials and music videos, and
roles include direction, image, art direction and editing; plus CD jackets,
VOGUE and Ryuko Tsushin art direction, and niDo textile design. Shown at the
Edinburgh International Film Festival and Anifest. Received Japan Media Arts
Festival jury recommendation. Now a freelance director.

036

キム・スンヨン
KIM SEUNG YONG

1968年滋賀県出身、在日コリアン三世。1997年、旅の途中にチベット問題と出会い衝撃を受け、持ち歩いていたビデオカメラで撮影を始める。チベット亡命政府の協力を得、ダライ・ラマ14世に10日間の同行取材を敢行。ロードムービー「チベットチベット」として完成させる。その後も中国雲南省やインドなど海外一人旅をテーマに作品を作り続けている。

1　Documentary – *Tibet Tibet* (2001)

2　Documentary – 「雲南 COLORFREE」
　　Yunnan COLORFREE (2007)

BELONG TO	ラゴス Ragos	CATEGORY	MV, CM, Short Movie, Animation
TOOLS	Final Cut	TEL	090 1919 3953
		E-MAIL	taro_2524@hotmail.com
		URL	http://www.tibettibet.jp http://www.colorfree.jp

Third-generation Korean, born 1968 in Shiga, Japan. Shocked by the problems in Tibet
on a trip in 1997, he began filming with a video camera he happened to have with him
and ended up spending 10 days conducting a traveling interview with the 14th Dalai
Lama, completed as the road movie "Tibet Tibet". He continues to make work about trips
abroad, in locations including Yunnan (China) and India.

037

木村敏子
TOSHIKO KIMURA

1978年生まれ。創形美術学校卒業。2002年8月ROCKET（原宿）にて初個展。2005年10月
LAPNET SHIP（原宿）にて個展を開催し、同年よりフリーランスとしてイラストレーションを中心
に活動中。映像作品、アパレル、雑誌、家電、ファブリックなどの各種プロダクトにアートワーク
を提供。

1   MV - Capitol K, *Can't Lie Down*
    (©VROOM SOUND RECORDS
    ©Faith&Industry, 2005)

2   MV - SOUTH, *Up Close And Personal*
    (©ponycanyoncYoung American,2006)

3   Short Movie - W+K 東京 LAB, *Voiceflux*
    (©w+k 東京 LAB 2007)

4   Original Work - Illustration

TOOLS	After Effects, Final Cut, Illustrator, Photoshop	CATEGORY	MV, CM, Short Movie, Animation, Product Design
		E-MAIL	toshiko.kimura @kemukujara.net
		URL	http://www.kemukujara.net

3

4

Born in 1978. Graduate of the Sokei Academy of Fine Art and Design. Had a first solo show at Rocket, Harajuku in August 2002 and from that year she became freelance, focusing on illustration. She supplies the artwork for a wide variety of projects including motion graphic works, apparel, magazines, consumer electronics and fabrics.

038

北山大介
DAISUKE KITAYAMA

1975年兵庫県神戸市生まれ。1995年アニメーションスタッフルーム入社。1999年「HELP!Design」にて映像部門「HELP! FILMS」設立後、映像部門を独立させ「orange films」としてスタート。2007年よりアニメーター前田久美子を迎えユニットとなる。CORNELIUS、カジヒデキ、HARCO、bonobos、アナ、migu、TAHITI80などのミュージックビデオ、LIVE VJなどを手がける。

1

2

| | MV – ANA, *NEXT* (compactsounds, 2007) | 3 | Opening Movie –
WORLD SOCCER NEWS "FOOT!"
(J SPORTS, 2007) |
| 2 | MV – ANA, *FLASH* (compactsounds, 2007) | 4 | MV – bonobos, *Someway* (Dreamusic, 2008) |

BELONG TO	オレンジフィルムス	CATEGORY	MV, TV, CM, LIVE VJ,
	orange films		Short Movie, Animation,
			DVD Contents
TOOLS	After Effects,		
	Final cut,	TEL / FAX	+81 (0)3 3463 5596
	LightWave 3D,		+81 (0)3 3463 5596
	Illustrator,		
	Photoshop	E-MAIL	orange_films@mac.com
		URL	http://www.myspace.com/
			orange_films

3

4

Born in Kobe in 1975. Started working at Animation Staffroom in 1995. After founding the Help! Films division of Help! Design in 1999, he started an independent film specialty division called "orange films". In 2007 he brought in animator Kumiko Maeda to make it a unit. Involved in music videos and Live VJing for people like Cornelius, Hideki Kaji, Harco, bonobos, Ana, migu and Tahiti80.

039

木津裕史
HIROSHI KIZU

1976年生まれ。京都芸術短期大学映像科卒。在学中、伊藤高志の実験映像と長谷川和彦の「太陽を盗んだ男」とエヴァンゲリオンにやられる。2001年MTV JAPAN入社。以後5年にわたり番組オープニングやStation IDなど、これでもかというほど創ることになる。2006年MTV VIDEO MUSIC AWARDS JAPAN 2006のイベント映像をトータルでディレクション。その後、MTV JAPANを退職。2007年P.I.C.S.に所属。

1

2

1	Event Movie – MTV Video Music Awards 2006 Opening & Nomination (©MTV NETWORKS JAPAN, 2006) Director: 木津裕史 Hiroshi Kizu, Motion Graphics: 小松好幸 Yoshiyuki Komatsu, Design: 広岡毅 Tsuyoshi Hirooka, Mechanic Design: 大久保淳二 Junji Okubo, CG: spice inc., Camera: 佐久間新二 Shinji Sakuma, Light: 斉藤卓 Taku Saito, Sound: 田中克明 Yoshiaki Tanaka, 木津裕史 Hiroshi Kizu, 未映子 Mieko, Model: 比嘉愛未 Manami Higa, 藤本征史郎 Seishiro Fujimoto,	令 Rei, 鉄平 Teppei, Producer: 日比野緑 Midori Hibino	3	OAP –「テレビ東京 PVTV 番組 Opening」TV Tokyo PVTV Opening（制作：スワン・ソング swan song） Director+Motion Graphics+Edit: 木津裕史 Hiroshi Kizu, CG: ジーニーズアニメーションスタジオ JINNI'S Animation Studios, Sound: 田中克明 Yoshiaki Tanaka, Producer: 上里滋 Shigeru Agari, Production by P.I.C.S.

2 Web Site Opening –「すらすらニュース」Sura Sura News
(©2007 INFOBAHN / P.I.C.S.) http://slasla-news.com/
Director+Motion Graphics+Edit+Sound:
木津裕史 Hiroshi Kizu, Animation: 村田翔 Sho Murata, 寺部晶 Akira Terabe
Producer: 松居秀之 Hideyuki Matsui / 寺井弘典 Hironori Terai, Production by INFOBAHN / P.I.C.S.

4 MV – 椎名林檎×斎藤ネコ『平成風俗大吟醸』DVD

BELONG TO	P.I.C.S.	CATEGORY	MV, On Air Promotion,
			CM, Motion Graphics,
TOOLS	Mac Pro,		Sound
	After Effects,		
	Illustrator,	TEL / FAX	+81 (0)3 5785 1780
	Photshop,		+81 (0)3 5785 1784
	Final Cut Pro,		
	Avid,	E-MAIL	post@picsco.net
	Ableton Live,	URL	http://www.picsco.net
	Gibson SG		

3

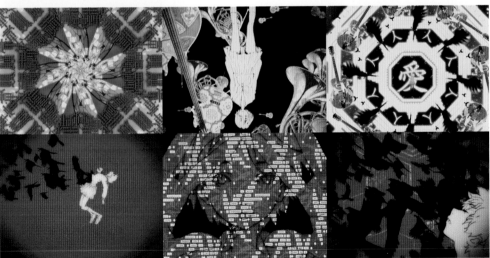

4

Video「ギャンブル」Ringo Shena × Neko Saito,
HEISEI FUZOKU DAIGINJO:DVD VIDEO, Gambling
(©EMI Music Japan Inc., 2007)
Director+Motoin Graphics+Edit: 木 津 裕 史 Hiroshi
Kizu, Animation: 花 ひ な 子 Hinaco Hana, 木野小太
郎 Kotaro Kino, CG: 針 生 悠 佝 Hariu Yuji, HAKKE
Design: 広岡毅 Tsuyoshi Hirooka, Cooperation: 田中
克明 Yoshiaki Tanaka, Producer: 松 居 秀 之 Hideyuki
Matsui, Production by P.I.C.S.

Born in 1976. Graduated from Kyoto College of Art. Always a student, he is
moved by Takashi Ito's experiments, Kazuhiko Hasegawa's "The Man Who
Stole the Sun", and Evangelion. Began working at MTV JAPAN in 2001 and was
involved in things like openings and station IDs. Directed visuals for the entire
2006 MTV Music Awards Japan. After that he left MTV and joined P.I.C.S. in
2007.

040

児玉裕一
YUICHI KODAMA

1975年生まれ。東北大学理学部化学系卒業。大学在学中より仙台にて映像制作の活動を開始。広告代理店勤務を経て独立。以後、フリーディレクターとしてCM、MVなどの演出を手がける。2006年CAVIARに参加。

1

2

I	CM –Vidal Sasoon Collaboration Video 安室奈美恵 Namie Amuro, *NEWLOOK* (P&G, avex, 2008)	3	MV – 東京事変 Tokyo Jihen, *OSCA* (EMI Music Japan Inc., 2007)
2	MV – RIP style VAIO "RIP SLIME", *I.N.G* (Warnaer Music Japan, 2007)	4	WEB – *UNIQLOCK* (UNIQLO, 2007)

BELONG TO	キャビア Caviar Limited	CATEGORY	MV, CM, Short Movie, Animation, Motion Graphics
TOOLS	After Effects, Final Cut, CINEMA 4D, 3ds Max, Shake	TEL / FAX	+81 (0)3 3791 9300 +81 (0)3 3791 9310
		E-MAIL URL	meetme@caviar.ws http://www.caviar.ws

3

4

Born in 1975. Graduated from the Tohoku University Department of Chemistry, Faculty of Science. Began making motion graphics while still a student in Sendai. After working for an advertising agency, he became freelance. He is involved in directing commercials and music videos. Became a member of Caviar in 2006.

041

古賀学
MANABU KOGA

1972年佐世保市生まれ。「ペッパーショップ」の名前でフリーペーパー編集発行、村上隆の初期作品や宣伝のデザインワーク（1993〜1997）、アートディレクション、キャラクターデザインを手がける。2004年から水中で女性を撮影した映像作品を制作している。現在、プロデュースユニットNORISHIROCKSと「水の中の女の子」をテーマしたアートプロジェクト「&a water／アンダーウォーター」を展開中。

1

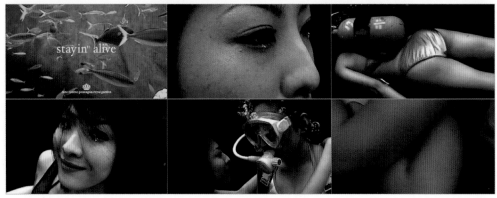

2

1   MV – &a water 01: *Guppy*
(©&a water. Manabu Koga. NORISHIROCKS.
2007)

2   MV – DATE COURSE PENTAGON ROYAL
GARDEN, *STAYIN' ALIVE*
(TRIAD / Columbia Music Entertainment,
2004)

3   MV – &a water 02: *White*
(©&a water. Manabu Koga. NORISHIROCKS.
2007)

4   MV – 「東京キャ☆バニー」
Tokyo Ca ☆ Bunny × &a water
(©&a water. Manabu Koga. NORISHIROCKS.
2008)

BELONG TO	アンダーウォーター &a water	CATEGORY	MV, CM, Short Movie
TOOLS	After Effects, Final Cut, Premiere	TEL / FAX	+81 (0)3 5452 7666 +81 (0)3 5452 7669 (D&N Planning)
		E-MAIL URL	underwater@dandn.co.jp http://andawater.jp/

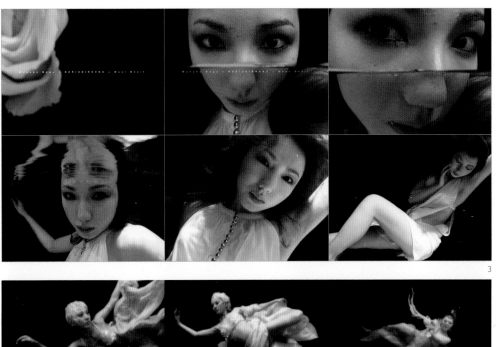

Born in 1972, Sasebo. Edits and publishes the free paper "Pepper Shop", involved in designing some of Takashi Murakami's early works and advertisements (1993-1997), does art direction and character design. Since 2004 has been making motion graphic works of women under water. He and NORISHIROCKS are a production unit developing a "women underwater" themed art project called "&a water/ underwater".

042

小島淳二
JUNJI KOJIMA

1966年生まれ。1995年日本初のモーショングラフィックススタジオ teevee graphics 設立。ディレクターとして CM、MV、ブロードキャストデザインなどジャンルを越えて多くの印象的な映像作品を生み出している。また、ラーメンズの小林賢太郎との映像ユニット NAMIKIBASHI としても活動中で、Jam Films 2 の 1 本として劇場公開された「机上の空論」では、RESFEST2003 にて AUDIENCE CHOICE AWARD を受賞。オリジナル DVD 『VIDEO VICTIM 1,2』『日本の形』を発表。

1

2

| 1 | MV – RYUKYUDISKO, *NICE DAY feat.BEAT CRUSADERS* (©Ki/oon Records Inc., 2007) | 3 | CM –au, *INFOBAR* (2003) |

1   MV – RYUKYUDISKO, *NICE DAY feat.BEAT CRUSADERS* (©Ki/oon Records Inc., 2007)

2   CM – 資生堂 "TSUBAKI / 美髪ヘアマスク" Shiseido Co., Ltd., *TSUBAKI / Bigami Hair Mask* (Shiseido Co., Ltd., 2007)

3   CM –au, *INFOBAR* (2003)

4   SHORT FILM – *The Japanese Tradition -SUSHI-*, DVD "VIDEO VICTIM 2" 収録 (2002)

BELONG TO	ティ・ビィ・グラフィックス teevee graphics	CATEGORY	CM, MV, Broadcast Design, Web
		TEL / FAX	+81 (0)3 3400 6455 +81 (0)3 5468 7048
		E-MAIL URL	kojima@teeveeg.com http://www.teeveeg.com

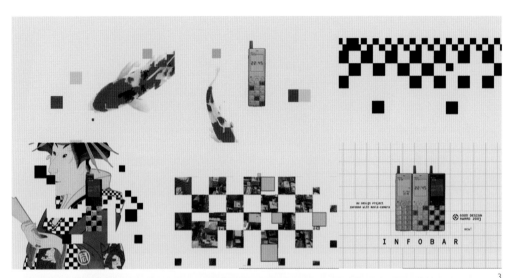

3

4

Born in 1966. In 1995, he founded "teevee graphics", the first motion graphics studio in Japan. His impressive genre-defying directorial works have appeared one after the next, in fields including commercials, music videos and broadcast design. He is also involved in Kentaro Kobayashi (of Rahmens)'s video group "NAMIKIBASHI" and his "Kijo no Kuron", a segment of the omnibus "Jam Films 2" won an award at RESFEST 2003. He released the videos "VIDEO VICTIM 1,2" and "THE JAPANESE TRADITION".

043

小島淳平
JUNPEI KOJIMA

1973年東京生まれ。武蔵野美術大学短期大学部専攻科卒業。ACA企画演出部、葵プロモーション企画演出部を経て、2004年「THE DIRECTORS GUILD」を設立。TV-CMの演出を中心に、ショートムービーやMVの演出も手がける。

1

2

1 CM - ダンディハウス「ビリヤード」 Dandy House, *billiards* (SHAPE UP HOUSE CO.,LTD., 2007)	3 CM - グランツーリスモ5 プロローグ「CHANGE」 GRAN TURISMO 5 *Prologue*, CHANGE (Sony Computer Entertainment Inc., 2007)
2 CM - BODY WILD「パンツRUN」 *Pants Run* (GUNZE Limited, 2007)	4 CM - AXE デオドラントスプレー *Bungee* (Unilever Japan, 2008)

BELONG TO	ザ・ディレクターズ・ギルド THE DIRECTORS GUILD	CATEGORY	CM, MV, Short Movie
		TEL / FAX	+81 (0)3 5712 5672 +81 (0)3 5712 5673
		E-MAIL	tdg_info@d-guild.com
		URL	http://www.d-guild.com/

"プレイステーション 3" 専用ソフトウェア「グランツーリスモ 5 プロローグ」（株式会社 ソニー・コンピュータエンタテインメント）

©2007 Sony Computer Entertainment Inc. Manufacturers, cars, names, brands and associated imagery featured in this game in some cases include trademarks and/or copyrighted materials of their respective owners. All rights reserved. Any depiction or recreation of real world locations, entities, businesses, or organizations is not intended to be or imply any sponsorship or endorsement of this game by such party or parties.

3

4

Born in Tokyo in 1973. Completed the one-year post-graduated from Musashino Art University junior college of Art and Design. He worked in production and direction at ACA, subseguently worked at Aoi Advertising Promotion, and in 2004 became one of the founders of THE DIRECTORS GUILD. Focusing on the direction of TV commercials, he is also involved in directions of short movies and music videos.

044

小嶋貴之
TAKAYUKI KOZYMA

1972年名古屋生まれ。人知れずジャッキーチェンを目指すも挫折。劇映画、実験映画などを迂回して現在に至る。MV制作本数100本超。

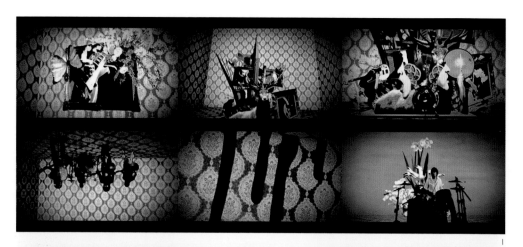

1

2

1   MV – GHEEE, *Beautifl stungun*
    (©JULY RECORDS, 2007)

2   MV – ザ・キャプテンズ「薔薇の檻」
    The Captains, *Bara no Ori*
    (©K&A CO.,LTD., 2007)

3   MV – LITE, *tomorrow*
    (©UK.PROJECT, 2007)

4   MV – 田中雄一郎「殴者」
    Tanaka Yuichiro, *Nagurimono*
    (©ground records, 2007)

TOOLS	After Effects, Photoshop, Premiere	CATEGORY	MV, CM, Short Movie, Animation
		TEL / FAX	080 5405 1696 +81 (0)3 3372 0773
		E-MAIL	kozyman_v_d@ybb.ne.jp

3

4

Born in Nagoya in 1972. He made his way to where he is today by a route that He had a secret aspiration to be Jackie Chan but his hopes were thwarted. He made his way to where he is today through fiction movies and experimental movies. He has made more than 100 music videos.

045

黒田賢
SATOSHI KURODA

1977年兵庫県生まれ。2006年P.I.C.S.入社。CMやMV、On Air Promotionなどの企画・演出に加え、CGアニメーション・モーショングラフィック制作までトータルに行う。オリジナル作品「あるひとつの方向性」が2006年文化庁メディア芸術祭 アニメーション部門 短編にて審査員推薦作品に選出、RESFEST 2006 World Tourにて作品上映。

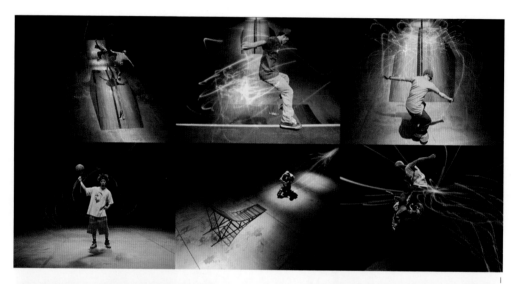

1

2

1 VP – Panasonic Lumix FX500「フリースタイルスポーツ篇」, *free style sports*
Director + CG: 黒田 賢 Satoshi Kuroda, Camera: 奥口睦 Makoto Okuguchi, Light: 西尾慶太 Keita Nishio, VE: 服部泰之 (Yasuyuki Hattori, Art: 吉田昌也 Masaya Yoshida, Hair Make: 新宮利彦 Toshihiko Shingu, Music: ORGA, CG: 岩橋正記 Masaki Iwahashi, Producer: 安藤貴久 Takahisa Ando, 寺井弘典 Hironori Terai, 清水忠 Tadashi Shimizu, Production by P.I.C.S.

2 MV – WAGDUG FUTURISTIC UNITY, *ILL MACHINE* (×ULTRA BRAiN)
(©Sony Music Japan International Inc., 2007)
Director + CG: 黒田賢 Satoshi Kuroda, CG: 藤井雄 Yu Fujii, 岩橋正記 Masaki Iwahashi, 村上仁志 Hitoshi Murakami, ED: 渡邊摩耶 Maya Watanabe , MA: 蓑輪直子 Naoko Minoya, Producer: 岩佐和彦 Kazuhiko Iwasa, Production by P.I.C.S.

3 MV – L-VOKAL「万歳」, *Banzai*
(©UNIVERSAL MUSIC K.K., 2008)
Director + CG: 黒田賢 Satoshi Kuroda
CG: 岩橋正記 Masaki Iwahashi, 山本正太 Syota Yamamoto, ED: 高崎馨 Kaoru Takasaki, MA: 井上武俊 Taketoshi Inoue, Producer: 松居秀之 Hideyuki Matsui, Production by P.I.C.S.

BELONG TO	P.I.C.S.	CATEGORY	MV, OAP, CM
TOOLS	3ds Max, After Effects, Premiere	TEL / FAX	+81 (0)3 5785 1780 +81 (0)3 5785 1784
		E-MAIL	post@picsco.net
		URL	http://www.picsco.net

3

4

4   MV - GREAT ADVENTURE, *THE AUDIENCE*
(©EMI Music Japan Inc., 2007)
  Director+CG: 黒田賢 Satoshi Kuroda,
  Camera: 小 川 ミ キ Miki Ogawa, CG: 岩 橋 正 記
  Masaki Iwahashi, 山下裕智 Hirotomo Yamashita,
  Animation: 吾 郷 葉 月 Hazuki Ago, Pro.下 田 伸 貴
  Nobutaka Shimoda, Production by P.I.C.S.

Born in Hyogo Prefecture, 1977, joined P.I.C.S. in 2006. In his production and direction of commercials, music videos and on-air-promotions etc, he manages every aspect, including making CG animation and motion graphics. His original work "One of the Ways" was commended by the jury at the Japan Media Arts Festival in the animation / short film division, and was shown on the RESFEST 2006 World Tour.

046

くろやなぎてっぺい
TEPPEI KUROYANAGI

1979年愛知県生まれ。広告デザイン専門学校（KDPS）を卒業後、フリーランスとして活動開始。デザイン業務を行う傍ら、映像音楽・アニメーション・ファッション・ゲームなど多種多様な仕事を手がける。ロサンゼルス映画祭やSiggraphなどの国際映画祭をはじめ、国内外のプロジェクトに参加。

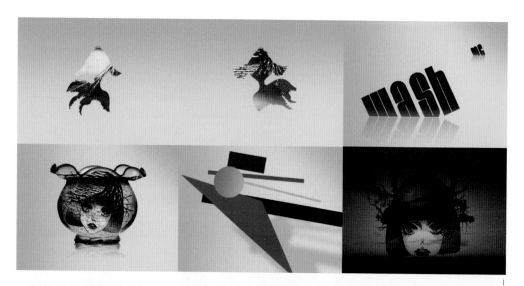

1

2

1	MV – 椎名林檎 & 齋藤ネコ「浴室」 Ringo Shiina & Neko Sito, *Yokushitsu* (©EMI Music Japan Inc., 2007)	3	GAME – *SPACE INVADERS EXTREME* (©TAITO CORP. 1978, 2007)
2	MV – ストレイテナー STRAIGHTENER, *ALIBI* (©EMI Music Japan Inc., 2007)	4	VIDEO ART – *if time pass* (©Teppei Kuroyanagi × Kayaku Project, 2007)

TOOLS	After Effects, Premiere, Illustrator, Photoshop	CATEGORY	MV, Video Art, Broadcast Design, Animation, Game
		TEL / FAX	090 1728 9825
			+81 (0)3 6762 5445
		E-MAIL	info@nipppon.com
		URL	http://nipppon.com

3

4

Born in Aichi Prefecture in 1979. After graduating from Koukoku Design Professional School (KDPS), he began working freelance. Aside from design business, he also does work in multiple areas including motion graphics for music, animation, fashion and games. Involved in international film festivals like Los Angeles and Siggraph, and in projects both at home and abroad.

047

牧鉄兵
TEPPEI MAKI

1978年大阪生まれ。映像作家。近作はDJ KENTARO「Shuriken Cut」「Tasogare High way High」、
OMODAKA「Kokiriko bushi」、KASKADE「BE STILL」、FUURI「NANA SONG」などのMV。
膨大な作画を軸にしたアニメーションを主体にRESFESTなどへの出展、MV、TV番組のタイトル
映像、3DCGなど幅広い映像表現を行う。

3

I   MV - OMODAKA, *Kokiriko bushi*
     (©Far East recording, 2007)

2   TV - ZAMURAI TV 弐
     「鎮座」*Chinza DOPENESS remix*
     (©SPACE SHOWER NETWORK, 2007)

3   Mobile Movie - *Docomo p903ix*

4   CM - *DVD magzine"BTTV"*

TOOLS   After Effects,
           3ds Max

CATEGORY   MV, CM, Animation, Manga

E-MAIL   info@chokusen.com
URL   http://www.chokusen.com/

2

3

4

Born Osaka, 1978. Motion graphic creator. Recent music videos include DJ Kentaro's
"Shuriken Cut" and "Tasogare Highway High", Omodaka's "Kokiriko bushi", Kaskade's
"Be Still" and Fuuri's "Nana Song". Focusing on movies made huge by all the animation,
he exhibits at festivals like RESFest, and is involved in a range of image expression,
including music videos, TV program title visuals, and 3-D CG.

048

メタファー
METAPHOR

永嶋敏之氏、金原崇人氏、増田一太郎氏の3人により2007年に設立されたデザイン＆エンジニアチーム。Web制作を中心に、映像、グラフィック、インスタレーションなど、その活動は多岐に渡る。「京都造形芸術大学ウェブサイト」「water展（21_21 DESIGN SIGHT 第2回企画展）への参加」など。松陰神社周辺にて地味に展開中。

1

2

1	CM – *Ex:beaute* (©Madre:X, 2008) Production: THE STRIPPERS, P.I.C.S., METAPHOR, Agency: AD GEAR, Director: 遠崎寿義 Hisayoshi Tohsaki, 橋本大佑 Daisuke Hashimoto, CD: 浅野矩美 Noriyoshi Asano, 亀井尚裕 Takahiro Kamei	2	Opening Movie – KyotoZokei「京都造形芸 術大学ウェブサイト」*Kyoto University of Art and Design Website* (Kyoto University of Art and Design) Production: 岡本彰生 Akio Okamoto	3 Original Work – *haohao* 4 Original Work – *processing study 1*

TOOLS	Photoshop, Illustrator, Flash	CATEGORY	Animation, Installation
		TEL / FAX	+81 (0)3 5534 6398
			+81 (0)3 5534 6398
		E-MAIL	contact@metaphor.co.jp
		URL	http://www.metaphor.co.jp

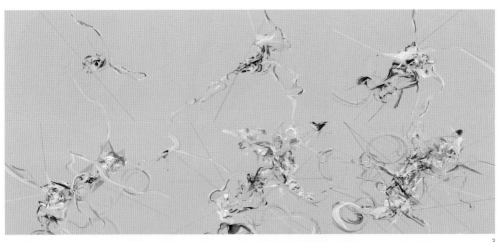

3

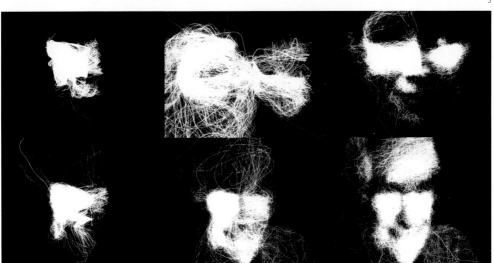

4

A design and engineering team founded in 2007 by Toshiyuki Nagashima, Takahito Kanehara and Ichitaro Masuda. Their activities are mainly focused on the web, and branch out into a variety of areas such as motion graphics, graphics, instalations, including the Kyoto University Arts and Design website and the "Water" exhibition at the second 21_21 Design Sight show. They work modestly around Shoin Shrine.

049

水野健一郎
KENICHIRO MIZUNO

1967年生まれ。鳥取大学工学部社会開発システム工学科中退。セツ・モードセミナー卒業。既視感と未視感の狭間にゆれるロマンチシズムを求めて、ドローイング、ペインティング、グラフィック、アニメーションなど、多種多様な手法で作品を制作。エキシビジョン中心のアーティスト活動のほか、ファッション・ブランドなどとジャンルを超えたコラボレーションを精力的に行う。

1

2

| I | Image Video – *DIET BUTCER SLIM SKIN* (©Kenichiro Mizuno, 2005) | 3 | VJ – KATHY+graf「炎のメリーゴーランド」 *Honoo no Merry Go Round* (©Kenichiro Mizuni, 2005) |
| 2 | MV – Lamb, *Orange Grove* (©SUCRE, 2005) | 4 | Exhibition – *Parking PARK* (©Kenichiro Mizuno, 200X) |

TOOLS	Illustrator, Photoshop, After Effects	CATEGORY	MV, CM, Short Movie, Animation
E-MAIL	jg2mfc00l@coral.ocn.ne.jp
URL	http://www1.ocn.ne.jp/~kmrpg/

3

4

Born in 1967. Dropped out of social development systems course (Engineering) at Tottori University. Graduate of "Setsu Mode" Seminar. Seeking romanticism in the interval between déjà vu and jamais vu, makes work with many and varied methods; drawing, painting, graphics, animation, etc. Makes art for exhibitions and tirelessly pursues genre-defying collaborations in fashion brands and other areas.

050

水尻自子
YORIKO MIZUSHIRI

1984年青森生まれ。女子美術大学デザイン学科卒業。卒業制作「かっぽ」が美術館収蔵作品となる。
手描きやコマ撮りアニメーションを中心に映像を制作し、Central East Tokyo 2007にて初個展「水尻
自子の"アニメは部屋で"展」、今年は「水尻自子のアニメマタニティ」展を開催した。

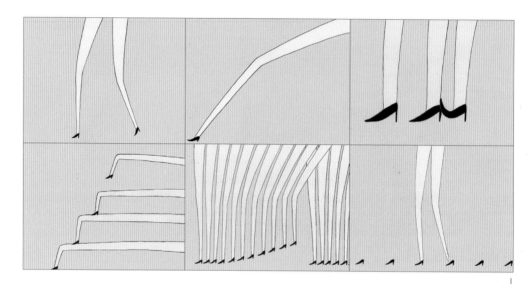

1

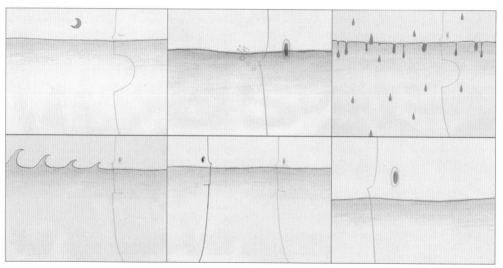

2

1   Animation –「かっぽ」 *Kappo*
    (©Yoriko Mizushiri, 2007)

3   Exhibition –「えにょぐ」 *Enyogu*
    (©Yoriko Mizushiri, 2007)

2   Exhibition –「ア シー ダズント テル マッチ」
    A sea doesn't tell much
    (©Yoriko Mizushiri, 2008)

4   VideoPodcast –「さすらいゾウさん」
    Sasurai Zosan
    (©Yoriko Mizushiri, 2007)

TOOLS	After Effects	CATEGORY	Animation, MV
		TEL / FAX	+81 (0)3 3705 5470
			+81 (0)3 3705 5471
		E-MAIL	yoriko.imoredy@nifty.com
		URL	http://www.geocities.jp/imoredy_yoriko/

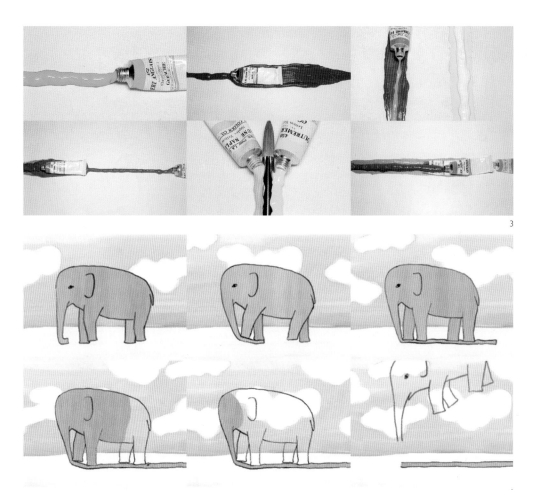

3

4

Σ

Born in Aomori, 1984. Graduated from Joshibi University of Art and Design, design degree. Her graduation work "Kappo" was made part of the museum's collection. Makes motion graphics using hand-drawings and stop-motion animation. Held first solo show, "Yoriko Mizushiri's 'Animation is done in your room'" at Central East Tokyo 2007. Soon she will have a show called "Yoriko Mizushiri's Animation Maternity".

051

木綿達史
TATSUSHI MOMEN

1973年生まれ。九州芸術工科大学（現 九州大学）中退。空気モーショングラフィックス（現 空気株式会社）設立。MV、CM、ゲームタイトルなどのディレクターを務める。アート系でもエンターテインメントでも広告でも、ぐっとくる映像を目指している。

1

2

BELONG TO	空気株式会社 KOO-KI CO.,LTD.	CATEGORY	MV, CM, Short Movie, Animation
TOOLS	After Effects, Maya	TEL / FAX	+81 (0)92 874 2020 +81 (0)92 874 2010
		E-MAIL URL	mom@koo-ki.co.jp http://www.koo-ki.co.jp

3

4

Born in 1973. Dropped out of the Kyushu Institute of Design (now called Kyushu University). Founded Koo-ki Motion Graphics. Director of music videos, commercials, game titles, etc. Whether creating for artistic, commercial, or advertising purposes, he aims at images that grab your attention in some way.

052

ムー°Cマジック
MOOD MAGIC

世界のアニメシーンで屈指の才能を発揮する保谷ひばり、ライブ映像やVJを手がける迫田悠、そして CG アニメーターの渡部暁の 3 人で構成され、System 7（UK）「Hinotori」のMV制作より活動を始める。

1　MV - System 7, *Hinotori*
　（©A-wave Records, ©Tezuka Productions,
　Wakyo Records / Music Robita)

2　VMC filler Movie - System 7, *Song For
　the Phoenix* (©A-wave Records, ©Tezuka
　Productions, ©Spaceshower TV, Wakyo
　Records / Music Robita)

TOOLS	After Effects, Maya, Illustrator, Photoshop	CATEGORY	MV
		TEL / FAX	+81 (0)422 49 9008 +81 (0)422 49 9009 (Wakyo Inc.)
		E-MAIL	moodmagic@wakyo.jp
		URL	http://www.sakotaharuka.com/moodmagic/

Hibari Hoya, one of the world's greatest motion graphic creators, Haruka Sakota, who is experienced in things like live footage and VJing, and CG animator Akira Watanabe form a three-person unit who began their work with the music video for System 7(UK)'s "Hinotori".

森田淳子
JUNKO MORITA

1971年神奈川県出身。多摩美術大学グラフィックデザイン科卒業。1995年葵プロモーション入社、2002年からフリーランスとして、TV-CMの演出を中心に、ショートムービーやMVの演出も手がける。2005年「THE DIRECTORS GUILD」参加。

1   CM – *Click Yahoo! Auctions?*
     (©Yahoo Japan Corporation., 2004)

2   MV – 風味堂「愛してる」
     Fumido, *Aishiteru*
     (©Victor Entertainment, INC. /
     Topcoat Music co., ltd., 2006)

3   MV – 井上陽水奥田民生「パラレル・ラブ」
     InoueYosuiOkudaTamio, *Pararel Love*
     (©FOR LIFE MUSIC ENTERTAINMENT,INC.&sic
     Sony Network Inc., 2006)

4   Mobile Movie – FOMA+RT「UFO 見たよ」
     UFO Mitayo
     (©NTT DoCoMo, Inc., 2004)

BELONG TO	ザ・ディレクターズ・ギルド	CATEGORY	CM, MV, Short Movie
	THE DIRECTORS GUILD		
		TEL / FAX	+81 (0)3 5712 5672
			+81 (0)3 5712 5673
		E-MAIL	tdg_info@d-guild.com
		URL	http://www.d-guild.com/

3

4

Born in Kanagawa Prefecture in 1971. Degree in Graphic Design from Tama Art University. Started working at Aoi Promotion in 1995 and became freelance in 2002, focusing on directing TV commercials while also involved in the direction of things like short movies and music videos. Became a member of THE DIRECTORS GUILD in 2005.

村上ヒロシナンテ
HIROSINANTE MURAKAMI

1975年生まれ。1996年九州造形短期大学デザイン学科クラフトデザインコース卒業。2001年、㈱広告研究所を経て、空気株式会社入社。主に、TV-CM、番組パッケージ、ゲームオープニングのディレクションを手がける。代表的な仕事に、セガ（ゲームタイトル・デモムービー）、台湾7-ELEVEN（TVCM一連）、横浜銀行ブランドビデオ、テレビ朝日（サッカー番組タイトル）、JCB（CI）ほか。

2

	Vision Image - Yahoo! ドーム ホークスビジョン用演出映像 Yahoo dome Hawks vision image for Hawks (2007)		CM - 台湾セブンイレブン Open 小將 Taiwan 7-Eleven open-chan 「心熱園」 (2007)
1		3	
2	Brand Video - 横浜銀行ブランドビデオ Brand Video for Bank of Yokohama (2007)	4	Game Movie - 「プロサッカークラブをつくろう！ヨーロッパチャンピオンシップ」 Pro Soccer Club Wo Tsukurou EUROPE CHAMPIONSHIP (©SEGA, 2005)

BELONG TO	空気株式会社 KOO-KI CO.,LTD.	CATEGORY	On Air Package, CM, Animation, CI, Game Opening Movie
TOOLS	After Effects, 3d studio Max	TEL / FAX	+81 (0)92 874 2020 +81 (0)92 874 2010
		E-MAIL	hirosinante@koo-ki.co.jp
		URL	http://www.koo-ki.co.jp

3

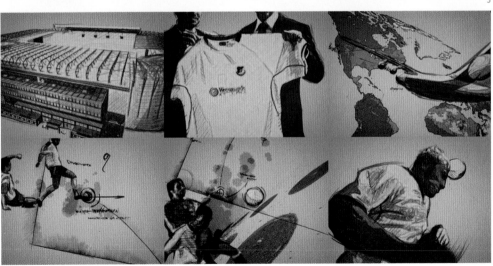

4

Born in 1975. Craft Design degree from Kyushu Zokei Art College in 1996. After the worked at Advertising Research Institute, joined KOO-KI in 2001. Mainly directs TV commercials, TV program packages and computer game openings. Work for SEGA (game titles, demo movies), Taiwan 7-Eleven (TV commercials), Yokohama Bank brand video, TV Asahi (Soccer program titles) and JCB (CI), etc.

村越陽平
YOHEI MURAKOSHI

1983年生まれ。2007年多摩美術大学美術学部グラフィックデザイン学科卒業。同年、株式会社博報堂入社。現在、株式会社HAKUHODO DESIGNにて、デザイナーとして勤務。広告のデザインだけでなく、個人的な活動としてアニメーションやイラストレーションなどを制作。準朝日広告賞、読売広告大賞入賞などの広告賞を受賞する一方で、東京国際アニメフェア日経エンターテイメント賞、文化庁メディア芸術祭審査員推薦作品入選、デジタルスタジアム出演など、映像の分野にも作品を展開している。

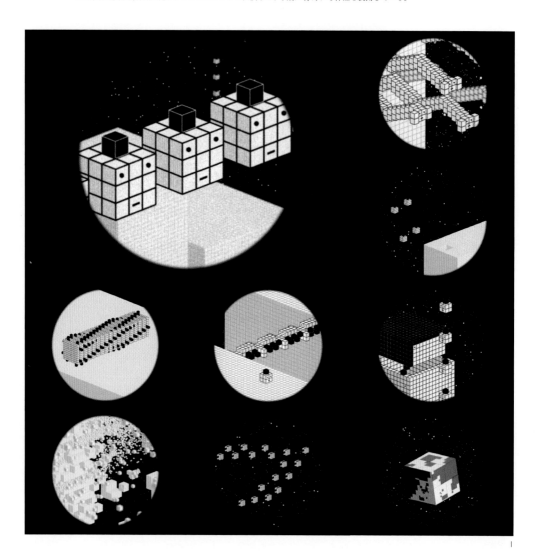

1   Animation – BLOCKMAN (2008)

2   Animation – IMOMUSHI (2005)

3   Animation – SMALLMAN LABOLATORY
    (2006)

TOOLS	After Effects, Final Cut	CATEGORY	Animation, Illustration, MV, CM
		E-MAIL	YOHEI.MURAKOSHI @hakuhodo.co.jp
		URL	http://www.ymweb.net/

2

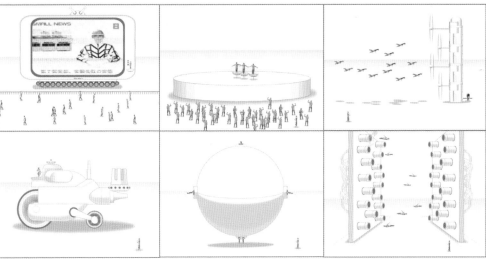

3

Born in 1983. Graphic Design degree from Tama Art University. A designer at Hakuhodo Design. He does not only commercial design, but also his own animation and illustration work. Has not only won prizes like the Asahi and Yomiuri Advertising Awards and the Nikkei Entertainment Award at the Tokyo International Anime Fair, his work has been shown on Digital Stadium and he works also in motion graphics.

056

長添雅嗣
MASATSUGU NAGASOE

1979年生まれ。武蔵野美術大学卒業後、teevee graphics入社。デザイナーとして数々のCM・MVを手がけた後、ディレクターとして活動。その作品は海外の映像フェスティバルでも多数紹介され、注目を集めている。CM・MVを中心に映画タイトルバックやVJ・グラフィック、またステージ映像演出やGUIデザインとモニターの内外問わず活動中。

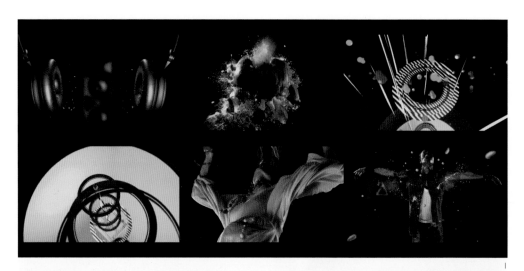

1

2

I MV – BOOM BOOM SATELLITES, *EASY ACTION*
(©Sony Music Records/gr8!, 2007)

2 MV – 髭 (HiGE)「溺れる猿が藁をもつかむ」
Oboreru Saru ga Waraomo Tsukamu
(©SPEEDSTAR RECORDS, 2007)

3 Broadcast Design –
MTV, *UK chart TOP10* (2007)

4 MV – MICRON' STUFF, *STROBO*
(©rhythm zone, 2007)

BELONG TO	ティ・ビィ・グラフィックス teevee graphics	CATEGORY	MV, CM, Opening Title, GUI Broadcast Design, VJ, WEB
TOOLS	After Effects, Photoshop, Illustrator, Lightwave 3D	TEL / FAX	+81 (0)3 3400 6455 +81 (0)3 5468 7048
		E-MAIL URL	nagasoe@teeveeg.com http://www.teeveeg.com http://vis.vc/#/12/

3

4

Born in 1979. Graduate of Musashino Art University, now at teevee graphics. Designer on many commercials and music videos, then a director. Works shown at many international festivals and attracted attention. Focusing on commercials and music videos, works both within and without the computer monitor, making title backgrounds, directing motion graphics for theater, GUI, and other things.

057

永田ナヲミ
NAOMI NAGATA

アニメーション作家。1978年生まれ。切り絵や砂を使ったコマ撮りアニメーションで、MVや個人作品を制作。2002年よりアニメーション上映企画団体 animation soup の運営スタッフとして、イベントの企画・運営も行っている。

1

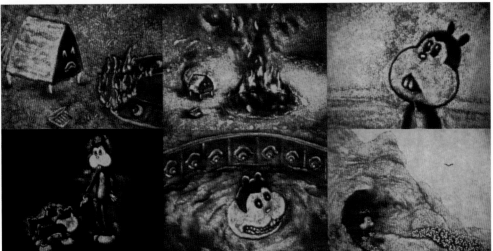

2

1   MV - キセル「砂漠に咲いた花」
Kicell, *Sabaku ni Saita Hana* (©Victor
Entertainment, Inc., 2003)

2   DVD- *VISIONS OF FRANK* - *FRANK*
(©PRESSPOP INC., 2005)

3   Opening Title - 「君に贈るうた」 *Kimini Okuru
Uta* (©NHK, 2006)

4   MV - 中山双葉「砂と女の子」
Futaba Nakayama, *Suna to Onnanoko*
(©Alchemy Records, 2007)

TOOLS	Final Cut	CATEGORY	Animation, MV, Illustration
		E-MAIL	nagata@animationsoup.com
		URL	http://www.animationsoup.com/nagata/

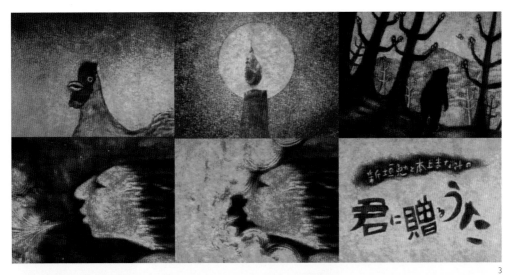

3

4

Animation creator. Born in 1978. She makes music videos and her own works in stop-motion animation using sand and paper cutouts. Since 2002 she has been involved in event planning and operation as a member of the management staff of the animation screening group "animation soup".

058

モンノカヅエ＋ナガタタケシ
TAKESHI NAGATA, KAZUE MONNO

1978年生まれ。1998年、京都造形芸術大学にて共同制作活動を始める。2001年、映像制作プロダクションで、ＴＶアニメのCGIを務める（ナガタタケシ）。2005年独立、映像制作ユニット「トーチカ」設立。映像制作を中心にグラフィックデザイン、ライブパフォーマンスなどを行う。現大阪電気通信大学デジタルアート・アニメーション学科講師。

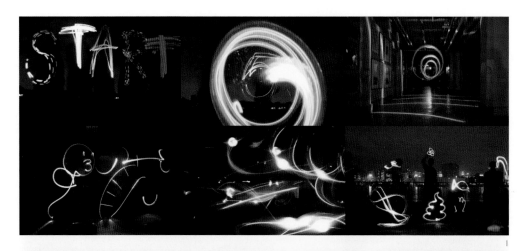

1	Short Film – *PIKA PIKA* (©TOCHKA, 2006)	3	Short Film – *Box Boy #1* (©TOCHKA, 2007)
2	Short Film – *PIKA PIKA 2007* (©TOCHKA, 2007)	4	STATION ID – *MILK JET #1* (©MTV-NETWORK, 2001)

| BELONG TO | トーチカ TOCHKA | CATEGORY | Animation, Short Film, MV, CM |
| TOOLS | Digital Still Camera, After Effects, 3ds Max, LightWave 3D, Premiere, Final Cut | E-MAIL URL | eleqitel@tochka.jp http://tochka.jp/ |

3

4

Born in 1978. Began working together in 1998 at the Kyoto University of Art and Design. In 2001, Takeshi Nagata worked at a motion graphic production company doing CGI for TV. Founded the motion graphics production unit "Tochka" in 2001. They do graphic design and live performance etc, focusing on motion graphic creation. Presently teaching Digital Art Animation at Osaka Electro-Communication University.

059

永戸鉄也
TETSUYA NAGATO

アーティスト、アートディレクター。1970年東京生まれ。高校卒業後渡米。帰国後、1996年より、音楽、書籍、広告の分野でアートディレクション、グラフィックデザイン、映像制作に携わる。2003年、第6回文化庁メディア芸術祭デジタルアート（ノンインタラクティブ）部門・優秀賞受賞。同年、トーキョーワンダーウォール公募2003年ワンダーウォール賞を受賞し東京都庁での個展を成功させるなどその活動は多岐にわたる。

1

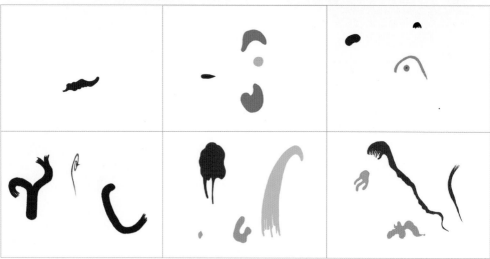

2

1 Shirt Movie – 「小さい日々」Chisai Hibi
   (2007)
   ポケットフィルムフェスティバル招待作品
   Invited for Pocket Film Festival
   Director, Music, Edit: Tetsuya Nagato

2 Mobile Movie – f-tone: Panasonic Mobile
   Phone P903ix Official Movie (2007)
   Line Animation+Music: Tetsya Nagato

3 Performance – Live Collage
   at Roppongi SuperDeluxe (2007)
   ビデオカメラを使いがその場で行う、切る・貼る・
   刻む・擦るなどの行為をプロジェクションする
   ライブパフォーマンス
   Photograph: Nagako Hayashi

4 Live – UA LIVE at Omotesando HIls (2007)

TOOLS	After Effects, Final Cut, Photoshop, Illustrator	CATEGORY	MV, CM, Short Movie, Animation
		TEL / FAX	+81 (0)3 5346 3689 +81 (0)3 5346 3689
		E-MAIL	info@nagato.org
		URL	http://www.nagato.org

3

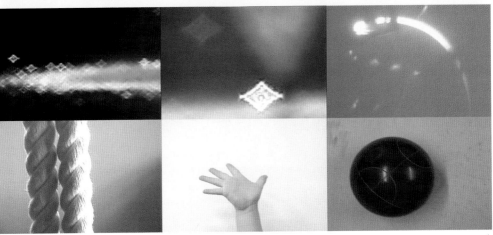

4

Born in Tokyo in 1970, he went to the United States upon graduating from high school. After returning to Japan in 1996, he began working in music and books, as well as commercial art design, graphic design and motion graphics. In 2003 he won the grand prize in the Digital Art Division (non-interactive) at the 6th Japan Media Arts Festival. The same year he submitted to Tokyo Wonder Wall and won the Wonder Wall Prize, holding a successful solo exhibition in Tokyo City Hall and progressing with a wide variety of other activities.

060

中村剛
TAKESHI NAKAMURA

1963年生まれ。多摩美術大学デザイン科卒業。1991年よりCM、MVなどのディレクションを開始。

1

2

Z

1	MV – 木村カエラ Kaela Kimura, *Jasper* (Columbia Music Entertainment, 2008)	3	CM – 「衛星劇場 15 周年記念 CM」 *Eisei / Eisei Gekijo 15 Aniversary* (NHK, 2007)
2	MV – RIP SLIME 「熱帯夜」 *Nettai-ya* (Warner Music Japan, 2007)	4	CM – *RUSS-K:07 A/W* (Crymson Co., Ltd, 2008)

BELONG TO	キャビア Caviar Limited	CATEGORY	MV, CM, Short Movie, Animation
TOOLS	After Effects, Final Cut, CINEMA 4D, 3ds Max, Shake	TEL / FAX	+81 (0)3 3791 9300 +81 (0)3 3791 9310
		E-MAIL URL	meetme@caviar.ws http://www.caviar.ws

3

4

Born in 1963. Design graduate of Tama University of Art. From 1991 began directing commercials, music videos, etc.

061

中尾浩之
HIROYUKI NAKAO

日本大学芸術学部放送学科卒業。2002年P.I.C.S.入社。躍動感溢れる実写作品の企画・脚本・演出を得意としながら、独自のスタイル「ライブメーション」による作品『スチーム係長』『trainsurfer』を発表し国内外で評価を得る。ショートフィルム、Web・CM・OAPなど幅広い映像作品を手がける。オリジナルドラマ「ZERO」DVDが2008年5月23日発売予定。また、「東京オンリーピック2008」（http://www.onlypic.org）の競技委員長など様々なメディアで新コンテンツのプロジェクトが進行中。

1

2

Z

1　Movie - オリジナルドラマ Original Drama, *ZERO*
(©2008 Zero Partners)
Original Concept+Script+Direcor: 中 尾 浩 之 Hiroyuki
Nakao, Camera: 小川ミキ Miki Ogawa, 中島純平 Zyunpei
Nakazima, VFX スーパーバイザー Supervisor: 佐竹淳 Jun
Satake, Assistant Director: 北川博康 Hiroyasu Kitagawa,
Light: 野村泰寛 Yasuhiro Nomura, Recording: 三 好 良
三 Ryozo Miyoshi, Art Design: 山下修侍 Syuji Yamashita,
Styling: 百井豊 Yutaka Momoi, 田村香代 Kayo Tamura,
Hair Make: 新宮利彦 Toshihiko Shingu, 青田真由美
Mayumi Aota, Editor: 正木良典 Yoshinori Masaki, Mixer:

嶋田美穂 Miho Shimada, CG: ジーニーズアニメーション
スタジオ JINNI'S Animation Studios., Motion Graphics:
フトン Futone Inc., Music: 戸田色音 Irone Toda/marond
K., Sound Design: 谷川義春 Yoshiharu Tanigawa

2.　CM - スパワールド SPA World Dr. SPA「新登場 離形
あきこ篇」*Shintoujou Hinagata Akiko*「号泣篇」
Goukyuu「泡文字篇」*Awamoji*
Direcor: 中尾浩之 Hiroyuki Nakao, Camera: 武村敏弘
Toshihiro Takemura, Light: 宮西孝明 Takaaki Miyanishi,
Art Design: 竹内美智代 Michiyo Takeuchi, Styling: 浅川

久美 Kumi Asagawa, Make: 松木麻紀子 Akiko Matsuki,
Styling+Make: 山本由美 Yumi Yamamoto, Producer: 津
秋 武 稔 Taketoshi Tsuaki, A&P: 電 通 関 西 DENTSU
Kansai + アットアームズ At Arms Inc.

3　Short Film - *Line* 文化庁委嘱事業若手映画作家育成プ
ロジェクト (©HIROYUKI NAKAO/VIPO)
Script+Direcor: 中尾浩之 Hiroyuki Nakao, Camera: 志
田貴之 Takayuki Shida, Light: 吉田恵輔 Keisuke Yoshida,
Recording: 稲田環 Tamaki Inada, Art Design: 吉田透 Toru
Yoshida, Styling: 藤田ユカ Yuka Fujita, Hair Make: 新宮

BELONG TO   **P.I.C.S.**

TOOLS   Premiere

CATEGORY   Movie, Drama, Short
             Film, Scenario, Original
             Contents, OAP, CM, MV

TEL / FAX   **+81 (0)3 5785 1780**
             +81 (0)3 5785 1784

E-MAIL   **post@picsco.net**
URL   **http://www.picsco.net**

3

4

利彦 Toshihiko Shingu, 青田真由美 Mayumi Aota, Music:
戸田色音 Irone Toda, Editor: 木村悦子 Etsuko Kimura,
Production: P.I.C.S.

4   Broadcast - NHK「カンゴロンゴ」〜カンゴローの
    四字熟語な生活〜 *Kangorongo ~Kangoro no
    Yojijukugo~*
    Direcor: 中尾浩之 Hiroyuki Nakao, CG: 瀬戸真人 Masato
    Seto, Animation: 木村元 Gen Kimura, 青柳麻美 Asami
    Aoyagi, 横山拓矢 Takuya Yokoyama, Producer: 平賀大介
    Daisuke Hiraga, Production: P.I.C.S.

Broadcasting graduated from Nihon University College of Art, Broadcasting
Department. Joined P.I.C.S. in 2002. Produces, writes and directs live action
photography. Internationally praised "Steam Head" and "trainsurfer" use his
"livemation" style. A broad production and direction range including short
films, web, commercials and on-air-promotions. On May 23rd will release
"Zero", an original drama DVD. Chairperson of "Tokyo Only Pictures 2008", he
also makes "new content" projects in various media.

z

062

ニコグラフィックス
NICOGRAPHICS

1979年生まれの泰永優子（やすなが・ゆうこ）と村井達雄（むらい・たつお）によるクリエイティブ・ユニット。仙台の大学在学時にコンビを組み、地方CM、テレビ番組などの制作に携わる。2003年には活動拠点を東京に移し、アニメーション制作、CG制作、CDジャケットデザイン、MVなどを幅広く手がける。

1

2

Z

| TOOLS | After Effects, Final Cut | CATEGORY | MV, CM, Animation |
| | | E-MAIL | nicogra@mac.com |

3

4

A creative unit made up of Yuko Yasunaga and Tatsuo Murai, both born in 1979.
They joined up while still university students in Sendai and began working on local
commercials and TV programs. In 2003, they moved their base of activities to Tokyo and
involved in a wide range of work, including animation, CG, CD cover design and music
videos.

063

西郡勲
ISAO NISHIGORI

1975年生まれ。文化学院高等部美術科在学中にCGを駆使したVJを始める。1995年MTV Station-IDコンテストグランプリ受賞をきっかけにMTV JAPAN入社。クリエイティブプロダクションP.I.C.S.を経て現在フリーランス。Siggraph、Promax & BDAなど多数受賞。文化庁メディア芸術祭アニメーション部門 優秀賞受賞、エジンバラ国際映画祭／広島国際アニメーションフェスティバル作品招待ほか。

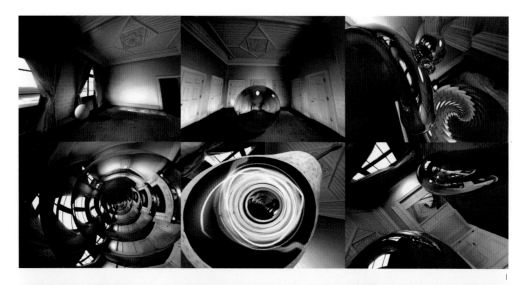

1

2

1　MV – ACIDMAN, *Walking Dada*
　Director+CG: 西郡勲 Isao Nishigori,
　CG: 米澤拓也 Takuya Yonezawa
　(©EMI Music Japan Inc., 2007)

2　MV – ACIDMAN, UNFOLD
　Director+CG: 西 郡 勲 Isao Nishigori, CG:
　米澤拓也 Takuya Yonezawa, Productin by
　P.I.C.S. (©EMI Music Japan Inc., 2007)

3　BRIDGESTONE adrenalin concept movie
　Director+CG: 西郡勲 Isao Nishigori, Productin
　by P.I.C.S.
　(©Bridgestone Corporation, 2007)

4　CM – パナソニック モバイルコミュニケーション
　ズ P905i「ビエラケータイ孔雀篇」Panasonic
　Mobile Communications P905i, *VIERA
　Keitai "Kujaku"*,

Director+CG: 西郡勲 Isao Nishigori,
Textile design: 阿南あす香 Asuka Anan, CG
Design: 米澤拓也 Takuya Yonezawa, CG:OMNIBUS
JAPAN, A&P: 電通 DENTSU INC. + PICT
(©Panasonic Mobile Communications Co.,
Ltd., 2008)

BELONG TO	P.I.C.S.management	CATEGORY	Live Action, 3DCG, Stage Image
TOOLS	LightWave 3D, 3ds Max, Photoshop, After Effects, Combustion	TEL / FAX	+81 (0)3 5785 1780 +81 (0)3 5785 1784
		E-MAIL	post.mg@picsco.net
		URL	http://www.picsco.net

3

4

Born in 1975. While Nishigori was attending the Bunka Academy High School (Department of Fine Art), he began VJing using computer graphics. After winning the grand prize at 1995 MTV Station-ID Contest, he began a job at MTV Japan. After working subsequently for the creative production firm P.I.C.S., he became freelance, a status he maintains presently. Nishigori has won numerous awards at competitions including Siggraph, Promax & BDA and the Japan Media Arts Festival. His work was invited to be screened at the Edinburgh International Film Festival and the Hiroshima International Animation Festival.

064

野本大
NOMOTO MASARU

1983年生まれ。日本映画学校に入学し、原一男・安岡卓治からドキュメンタリー制作を学ぶ。2年次に自傷癖のある女子高生を撮った「*@17」の演出を務める。卒業制作に、クルド難民の家族を追う「バックドロップ・クルディスタン」の企画を提出するも落選。撮影を続行するために、同校を中退し、自主制作として2008年本作品を完成。今後も、「個」の可能性を追い求める。

1　Documentary – *@17 (2004)

2　Documentary –「バックドロップ・クルディスタン」Back Drop Kurdistan
　(Back Drop Film, 2007)

TOOLS	DCR-TRV900, NV-GS70	CATEGORY	Documentary
		E-MAIL	nomoto_masaru58616 @yahoo.co.jp
		URL	http://www.back-drop- kurdistan.com/

2

Z

Born in 1983. Learned documentary filmmaking from Kazuo Hara and Takuji Yasuoka at the Japan Academy of Moving Images, in his sophomore year. He directed "*@17" about a high school girl with a self-mutilating problem. His proposal to follow a refugee Kurdish family for his thesis project "Back Drop Kurdistan" was rejected. He dropped out of school and finished it on his own in 2008. Continuing in his pursuit of the possibilities of "the individual".

065

株式会社ノングリッド
NON-GRID INC.

2000年設立。小池博史ほか10名のメンバーで構成されるクリエイティブプロダクション。Web、グラフィックデザインを軸に、近年ではファッションや音楽シーンでイベントやショップのインスタレーションを発表し、広いフィールドで持ち味を生かした活動を行っている。

I   Installation,Web - BIG SHADOW (©BIRD STUDIO
     / MISTWALKER, INC. All rights reserved..2006 ,
     ©Microsoft Corporation. All rights reserved..2006,
     ©BIG SHADOW PROJECT COMMITTEE.,2006)
     Creative Director: 内 山 光 司 Koshi Uchiyama
     (GT INC.), Art Director+Planner: 伊藤直樹 Naoki Ito (GT
     INC.), Producer: 工藤靖久 Yasuhisa Kudo (GT INC.),Planner
     +Director: 千房けん輔 Kensuke Senbo(exonemo), Planner:
     中村勇吾 Yugo Nakamura (tha), Director: 河村大馬
     Daima Kawamura(projector), Technical Advisor:
     マスダジュン Jun Masuda (mashstudio), Technical Support:
     コバヤシタケル Takeru Kobayashi (29970/ETHER), Technical

Director: 小池博史 Hiroshi Koike, Programmer: 前川峻志
Takashi Maekawa, Logo Design: 上神田彩子 Saiko Kamikanda
Web - Project Manager: 清水幹太 Qanta Shimizu, Producer:
足利建明 Tatsuaki Ashikaga, Designer: 藤牧篤 Atsushi
Fujimaki, Flash Engineer: 山春真 Shin Yamaharu, 高橋健一
Kenichi Takahashi, Engineer: 村山達也 Tatsuya Murayama
(saunaman)

2   Installation - BAYCREW*S VISION (©BAYCREW*S
     CO., LTD. All rights reserved., 2006)
     Creative Director: 小池博史 Hiroshi Koike, Project
     Manager: 森正徳 Masanori Mori, Designer: 伊藤和歌子

Wakako Ito, 鈴木翠 Midori Suzuki, Programmer: 前川
峻志 Takashi Maekawa

3   Installation - NON-GRID/IMG SRC new year party
     (©NON-GRID inc/IMG SRC, Inc. All rights reserved.,
     2007) Creative Director: 小池博史 Hiroshi Koike,
     Designer: 西薫徳 Takanori Nishi, 鈴木友晃 Tomoaki
     Suzuki, Programmer: 前川峻志 Takashi Maekawa, 松
     本典子 Noriko Matsumoto, System Engineer: 森正
     徳 Masanori Mori, 前川峻志 Takashi Maekawa, Video
     Engineer: 松本典子 Noriko Matsumoto, 宮地成太郎
     Sitarou Miyachi

TOOLS	Photoshop, Illustration, Flash, Dreamweaver, After Effects, MaxMsp, Jitter, Visual Studio	CATEGORY	Web, Motion Graphics, Illustration, Animation, Installation
		TEL / FAX	+81 (0)3 5428 8686 +81 (0)3 5428 8685
		E-MAIL URL	info@non-grid.com http://www.non-grid.jp

3

4

4   Web – REC YOU. (©Sony Marketing (Japan) Inc. All rights reserved., 2008)
Agency: GT INC, DENTSU INC., Creative Director+Art Director: 伊藤直樹 Naoki Ito (GT INC), Producer: 工藤靖久 Yasuhisa Kudo (GT INC), Project Manager: 遠藤正樹 Masaki Endo, Director: 清水幹太 Qanta Shimizu, 小池博史 Hiroshi Koike, Designer: 川嵜鋼平 Kohei Kawasaki, Flash+Programmer: 黒木圭太 Keita Kuroki, System Engineer: S2Factory, Inc., Movie: 平野太呂 Taro Hirano, 河村大馬 Daima Kawamura (projector), pictures inc., Movie Engine: Motion Portrait, Inc.

A creative unit founded in 2003 with 8 members including Hiroshi Koike. Focusing on web work, they are skilled at graphic design. Recently they have done installations in the fashion and music scenes; they cover a wide area of fields. They received the Gold Prize at the 2007 Cannes Lions Festival (advertising festival). Allied from 2006 with IMG SRC, Inc. (http://www. imgsrc.co.jp)

066

大原大次郎
DAIJIRO OHARA

1978年横浜生まれ。武蔵野美術大学基礎デザイン学科卒業後、2003年よりフリーランス。手作り感の強いグラフィックを中心に、これまでにASA-CHANG&巡礼、ピエール瀧、SAKEROCKなどのジャケットデザイン、アートワークを手がけたほか、POLYSICS、キセルのMV、TV番組のオープニングタイトル、アニメーションなどを制作。作品はWebサイト上にて、メイキングなどと併せて公開中。

1

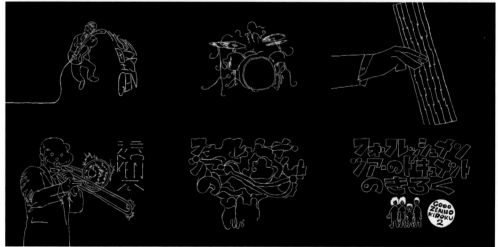

2

1	Opening Title – *FREAK OUT!* (©cool sound, SPACE SHOWER TV, 2007)	3	MV – POLYSICS 「コンピューターおばあちゃん」 *Computer Obaa-chan* (©ki/oon Records, 2007)
2	MV – SAKEROCK「ぐうぜんのきろく 2」 *Guzen no Kiroku 2* (©KAKUBARHYTHM, 2007)	4	MV – キセル「ビューティフルデイ」 *Kicell, Beautiful Day* (©KAKUBARHYTHM, 2008)

BELONG TO	オモンマ OMOMMA	CATEGORY	MV, Animation, Opening Title
TOOLS	After Effects, Final Cut	E-MAIL URL	ohara@omomma.in http://omomma.in

3

4

Born in Yokohama, 1978. Basic Design degree from Musashino Art University. Freelance from 2003. Focusing on graphics that feel hand-made, he has not only been involved in the jacket design and artwork for musicians like Asa-Chang & Junray, Pierre Taki and SAKEROCK, he has also worked on animation etc. for POLYSICS, KICELL's music videos and TV program openings.

067

大橋陽
YO OHASHI

1966年 北海道生まれ。青山学院大学中退。(株)スペースシャワーにて開局当初のスタッフとして、R&B系洋楽番組などの制作に携わる。その後 (有)ドゥ・ザ・モンキー、(株)ヴィジュアル・サインズを経て2000年に独立。フリーランスのディレクターとしてMV、ライブビデオなどを手がける。2004年より Rough & Tough Production 所属。

1

2

1	DVD - 安室奈美恵	3	MV - いきものがかり「青春ライン」
	NAMIE AMURO PLAY TOUR 2007		Ikimonogakari, Seishun Line
	(©AVEX ENTERTAINMENT INC., 2008)		(©Epic Records Japan Inc., 2007)
2	DVD - 木村カエラ「LIVE Scratch~上がってま	4	DVD - Every Little Thing,
	すってば TOUR @ 武道館」Kaela Kimura, Kaela		Every Little Thing 10th Anniversary Special Live at
	Kimura Live Scratch At Budokan		Nippon Budokan
	(©Columbia Music Entertainment Inc., 2007)		(©AVEX ENTERTAINMENT, 2007)

BELONG TO	ラフ&タフ プロダクション	CATEGORY	MV, Live Video
	Rough & Tough		
	Production	E-MAIL	y-ohashi@momo.so-net.
			ne.jp
TOOLS	Final Cut Pro	URL	http://rough-tough.com/

3

4

Born in Hokkaido in 1966. Dropped out of Aoyama Gakuin University. When he was first a staff member of Space Shower, he produced things like R&B music programs. After that he worked at Do The Monkey and Visual Science before working on his own. As a freelance director he has worked on music videos and live videos etc. In 2004 he became affiliated with Rough & Tough Production.

068

岡田尚志
TAKASHI OKADA

1999年より東京の下北沢を拠点にフリーランスでグラフィックとWebのデザインを始める。以来、主にflashを用い、さまざまな企業のWebサイトを手がける。また、手書きのイラストレーションによるタイポグラフィーと、Flashを用いたコラージュ的なモーショングラフィックおよびインタラクティブな作品をプライベートワークとして制作。

| Original Work – *trffdg* (2007)

2 Original Work – *DIE GELEGENTLICHEN MASHINEN FUR NEUEN GRAPHIK* (2006)

3 Original Work – *Monochrome garden* (2005)

4 Original Work – *what-scary-strange-amazing-complexity* (2006)

TOOLS	Flash, Photoshop, Sharp Pen	CATEGORY	Typography, Illustration, Animation, Interactive Motion
		E-MAIL	info@okadada.com
		URL	http://www.okadada.com

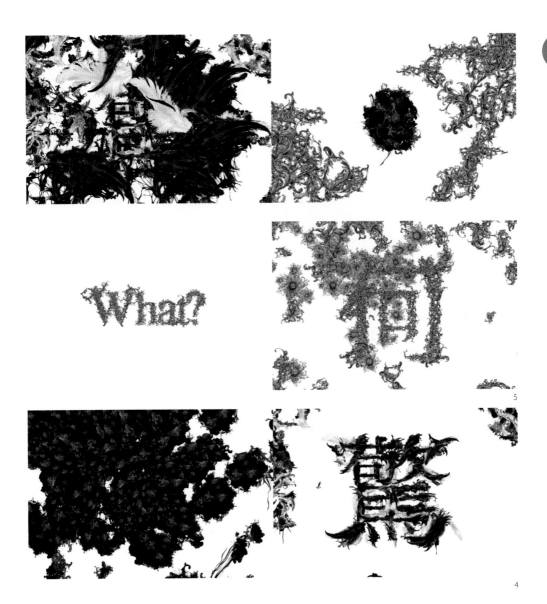

Since 1999, based in Tokyo's Shimokitazawa and doing freelance graphics and web design. Since then, he has been involved in jobs for various companies, mainly in Flash web content. Independently, he also makes collage-like motion graphic / interactive works using typography of hand-drawn illustrations and Flash.

069

オンナコドモ
ONNACODOMO

ミュージシャンDJ Codomo、アニメーション作家せきやすこ、イラストレーター野口路加の3人による異色のVJユニット。コンピュータグラフィックスや、録画素材を一切使用せず、ビデオカメラ、水、キッチン用品、文房具、おもちゃ、印刷物などを用いた独自のライブパフォーマンスを展開。主にバッファロー・ドーターのライブVJやSuperDeluxeでのイベントなどで活動中。

1

2

1　Exihibition – *onnacodomo Exhibition* 吉祥寺
　にじ画廊 Kichijoji Niji Garou (2007)

2　DVD – *The World of onnacodomo* (2007)

3　VJ – at Various Places (2007)

TOOLS	Video Camera, Light, Water, Spoon, etc...	CATEGORY	VJ, MV, Short Movie
		E-MAIL	onnacodomo@gmail.com
		URL	[DJ Codomo] http://web.mac.com/djcdm/
			[Ruka Noguchi] http://www.rukanoguchi.com/
			[Yasuko Seki] http://www.ysksk.com

3

Musician DJ Codomo, animator Yasuko Seki and illustrator Ruka Noguchi are a unique 3-person VJ unit. Without any computer graphics or pre-filmed materials, they put on a unique live performance using video cameras, water, kitchen utensils, stationery goods, toys, printed materials and other things. Mostly they are involved in their live VJ shows with Buffalo Daughter and events at SuperDeluxe.

070

大月壮
SOU OOTSUKI

1977年生まれ。東洋美術学校卒業。在学中、カナダ・ケベック大学デザイン科留学。CM制作会社を経て、2003年RESFESTにて映像作品「VIEW」を上映し、以降フリーランスとしてキャリアをスタートさせる。アパレルブランド「UNNON」への参加、CDジャケットデザインなどグラフィック制作とも関わる。現在は仕事を映像制作にシフトし、TV、MV、DVD、モバイルコンテツなど様々な映像制作の場で活動。2008年度より東洋美術学校非常勤講師。

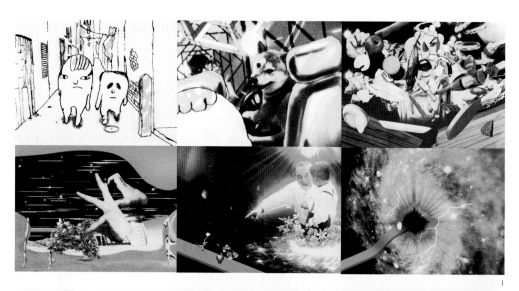

1

2

1	MV ~ APOGEE, *Just a seeker's song* (©Victor Entertainment, Inc., 2007)	3	TV ~ ZAMURAI TV 弐「鎮座」 *CHINZA DOPENESS remix* (©SPACE SHOWER NETWORK, 2007)
2	MV ~ NAWII, *OH!NAWII* (©Excite Music Entertainment co., Ltd., 2008)	4	WEB CM ~ *BROSTA TV AWARD 2008* (©BROSTA TV, 2008)

TOOLS	After Effects, Premiere, 3ds Max	CATEGORY	MV, CM, Short Movie, Animation
		E-MAIL	ootsuki@0m2.jp
		URL	http://www.0m2.jp/

3

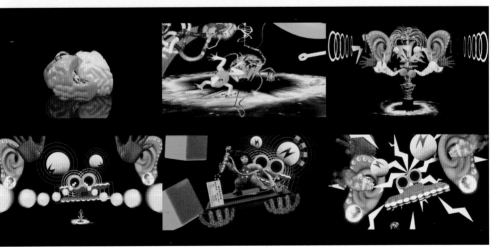

4

Born in 1977, degree from Toyo Institute of Art and Design. Studied design abroad at Quebec University. Worked at advertising company, then showed his motion graphics work "View" at 2003 RESFEST and started on his own. Makes graphics for CD jackets and the UNNON clothing brand. Now focused on motion graphic creation, his reach is broad, including TV, music videos, DVDs and cell phone content. From 2008, He started to lecture at Toyo Institute of Art & Design.

071

OTAS

1978年生まれ。1999年イメージスタジオ109ポストプロダクション事業部に入社。主にTV-CMの制作に携わる。2001年、ユナイティアに入社。プジョーのWebサイトなどのデザイン及びFlashによるモーションを担当する。2004年に渡米。Art Center College of DesignやOTISなどLAにある美術大学にてモーショングラフィックスについて学ぶ。現在は主にロサンゼルスでTV番組のメインタイトルやCMなどを制作している。

1

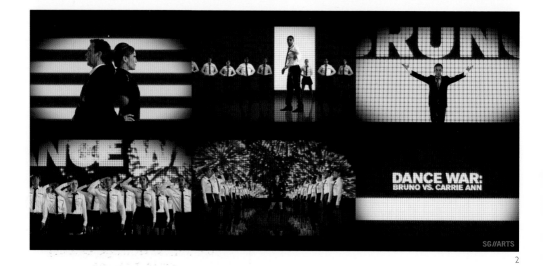

2

1   Promo – *OSCARS 07* (SG//ARTS, 2007)

2   Promo – *DANCE WAR* (SG//ARTS, 2007)

3   Main Title – *PROJECT RUNWAY*
     (SG//ARTS, 2007)

4   Main Title – *LAST COMIC STANDING*
     (SG//ARTS, 2007)

TOOLS	After Effects, Photoshop, Illustrator, CINEMA 4D	CATEGORY	Main Title, CM, MV, Game Movie
		TEL	+01 310 482 9018 (LOS ANGELES)
		E-MAIL	info@otas.tv
		URL	http://otas.tv

3

Art Center College Library
1700 Lida St.
Pasadena, CA 91103

Born in 1978. In 1999, he joined the post-production division of IMAGE STUDIO 109 and is engaged mainly in the production of TV commercials. He joined UNITEAIR Co. in 2001 and became in charge of motion using Flash and the Peugeot web site design. He moved to U.S. in 2004 and studied motion graphics at art schools in LA including the Art Center College of Design and OTIS. Currently engaged in producing main titles for TV shows and commercials mainly in LA.

072

パワーグラフィックス
POWER GRAPHIXX INC.

1996年より東京を拠点に制作活動を開始。グラフィックデザインと映像制作をメインに、様々なクライアントワークを手がけつつ、国内外のグラフィックメディアへ数多くのオリジナルワークを提供している。最近の主なクライアントワークとして『METAL GEAR SOLID PORTABLE OPS』（KONAMI）、65億人のサバイバル展（日本科学未来館）、『MUSIC VIDEO AWARDS08』（SPACE SHOWER TV）、『MTV Generic Package "CAVE"』（MTV JAPAN）などがある。

1

2

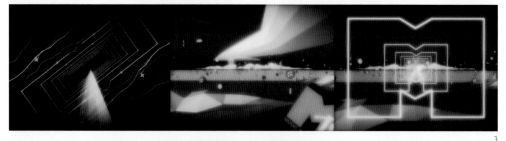

3

4

1	Short movie – *UNIQLO JUMP* Sound by Syn Entertainment	4	Opening Movie – *MG SAGA* (©1987, 2007 Konami Digital Entertainment Co.,Ltd.)	Entertainment Co.,Ltd.)

<table>
<tr><td>1</td><td>Short movie – UNIQLO JUMP
Sound by Syn Entertainment</td><td>4</td><td>Opening Movie – MG SAGA
(©1987, 2007 Konami Digital Entertainment
Co.,Ltd.)</td><td>Entertainment Co.,Ltd.)</td></tr>
<tr><td>2</td><td>Title Package – MVA07
Sound by 0mb
(©SPACE SHOWER TV, 2007)</td><td>5</td><td>Title Package – Love Music, Love Sports
Sound by 0mb
(©SPACE SHOWER TV, 2007)</td><td>7 Title Package – Make My Day
Sound by 0mb
(©MTV NETWORKS, 2007)</td></tr>
<tr><td>3</td><td>Title Package – MTV Generic PKG "CAVE"
Sound by Far East Recording
(©MTV NETWORKS, 2007)</td><td>6</td><td>Opening Movie – METAL GEAR SOLID PORTABLE OPS PLUS (©1987, 2007 Konami Digital</td><td>8 Title Package – ZOOM / ZOOM INT'L
(©SPACE SHOWER TV, 2006)</td></tr>
</table>

TOOLS	After Effects, Final Cut, CINEMA 4D	CATEGORY	MV, Short Movie, Animation
		TEL / FAX	+81 (0)3 6413 7021 +81 (0)3 6413 7022
		E-MAIL	support@power-graphixx.com
		URL	http://www.power-graphixx.com

5

6

7

8

POWER GRAPHIXX was established in Tokyo in 1996, and is focused on the graphic design and motion graphics fields. While proceeding with commercial work, POWER GRAPHIXX have also been actively contributing their original artwork to domestic and foreign design-related events, exhibitions and media. Recent projects include "METAL GEAR SOLID PORTABLE OPS" for KONAMI, "6.5 billions' Survival - Living, with Emerging Sciences-" for the National Museum of Emerging Science and Innovation, "Music Video Awards 2007" for Space Shower TV and "MTV Generic package 'CAVE'" for MTV Japan.

073

榊原澄人
SUMITO SAKAKIBARA

1980年生まれ。15歳で渡英。文化庁海外派遣制度を経て、RCA（英国王立美術大学院）を卒業後、パッションピクチャーズに所属。2006年フランスでアーティストレジデンスを経て、2007年帰国。今後、漫画・映像を中心に日本での活動を予定している。

1

2

1　Original -「淡い水の中」 *In The pale Water*
　　(©sumito sakakibara, 2007)

2　Original -「浮楼」 *Flow*
　　(©sumito sakakibara, 2005)

3　Original -「神谷通信」
　　Kamiya's Correspondence
　　(©sumito sakakibara, 2004)

4　Original -「カラス少年の事件簿」
　　Crow Boy Stories; Case of the Fox Kid
　　(©sumito sakakibara, 2003)

| TOOLS | Photoshop, After Effects | CATEGORY | Animation, Comics, Illustration, Children's Book |
| | | E-MAIL | sumito44@hotmail.com |

3

4

Born in 1980 and went to England at age 15. After doing overseas research for the Agency for Cultural Affairs, he graduated from the Royal College of Art and joined Passion Pictures. In 2006, he had an artists residency in France and returned to Japan in 2007. He plans to continue working in Japan, focusing on comics and motion graphics.

074

笹生宗慶
MUNECHIKA SASAO

1978生まれ。映像ディレクター。武蔵野美術大学彫刻学科卒業後フリーランス。TV番組、CM、MVなどのCGおよび実写映像のディレクションと制作を行っている。

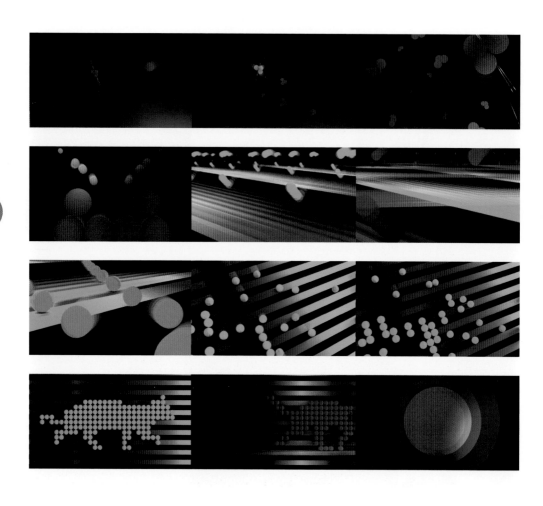

I MV - TRAKS BOYS, *starburst* (SWC, 2008)

BELONG TO	光 J HIKARU J	CATEGORY	TV-CG, MV, CM
TOOLS	Afetr Effects, Premiere, 3ds Max	TEL / FAX	+81 (0)3 5428 4778 +81 (0)3 5428 4779
		E-MAIL	cgsasao@gmail.com

Born in 1978 Motion graphic director. Began working freelance after graduating with a sculpture degree from Musashino Art University. CG and live action producer and director of TV programs, commercials, music videos, etc.

075

関根光才
KOSAI SEKINE

1976年生まれ。HAT演出部を経て、2008年2月よりフリーランスとしてマネジメントを「hybrid」に委託。2005年AdFestにて短編「RIGHT PLACE」を発表。以降RESFEST、エジンバラ国際映画祭などに参加し、各映画祭で多数の賞を受賞。2006年にはレインダンス映画祭CM「Daughter」で、カンヌ国際広告祭ヤングディレクターズアワードにてグランプリを含む3部門で受賞。同年、英「shots」が発表する世界広告ランキングでは、新人監督部門で世界1位を記録。

I　Short Film – *RIGHTPLACE* (2005)
　Production: HAT

2　レインダンス映画祭 Raindance Film Festival
　+DIESEL CM「Daughter 篇」*Daughter* (2006)
　Production: HAT

3　CM – 福岡人権尊重週間 Fukuoka City / Human
　Rights Week「黒板篇」*Blackboard* (2006)
　Agency: 電通九州 Dentsu Kyushu, Production:
　電通テック福岡 Dentsu Tec Fukuoka + VSQ

4　CM – 日本マクドナルド マックフルーリーダ
　ブルショコラ McDonald's Japan McFlurry
　Double Chocolate「ダンスミックス篇」*Dance
　Mix* (2007)
　Agency: 電通 Dentsu, Prodction: Engine Film

BELONG TO	hybrid (management)	CATEGORY	CM, MV, Short Film
TOOLS	Premiere, etc...	TEL / FAX	+81 (0)3 3420 1930 +81 (0)3 3420 1930
		E-MAIL	kosai@creativehybrid.com
		URL	http://www.kosai.info

3

4

Born in 1976. After working at HAT, Kosai became an independent director in February 2008, with management by 'hybrid'. After its premiere at AdFest in 2005, his short film "RIGHT PLACE" was screened and received many awards at festivals such as RESFEST and Edinburgh International Film Festival. In 2006, "Daughter" a commercial for Raindance Film Festival won 3 awards including 'Grand Prix' at Cannes Lions Young Directors Award. In the same year, the UK advertising publication "shots" ranked him 1st among the young directors in the world.

076

柴田大輔
DAISUKE SHIBATA

1973年、神戸生まれ。早稲田大学、桑沢デザイン研究所を卒業。1997年、電通テック企画演出部入社。2002年から1年半ほど休職し、L.A渡米。帰国後、電通テックに復職。2006年4月に電通テックを退職。5月から「THE DIRECTORS GUILD」に参加。TV-CMの演出を中心に、ショートムービーやMVの演出も手がける。

I

2

1　CM－「ロングヘアーカンフーマン－レスキュー」
　LONG HAIR KUNG-FU MAN, Rescue
　(©BANYU PHARMACEUTICAL CO.,LTD.
　Merck & CO., INC., 2007)

2　CM－Regain「リゲイン的出社風景」
　Regain, Regain teki Shusha-fukei
　(©DAIICHI SANKYO HEALTHCARE CO.,LTD.
　2007)

3　CM－GEORGIA「会議」*Meeting*
　(©Coca-Cola (Japan) Company, Limited., 2008)

4　CM－GEORGIA「キャンプ」*Camping*
　(©Coca-Cola (Japan) Company, Limited., 2008)

BELONG TO   ザ・ディレクターズ・ギルド
THE DIRECTORS
GUILD

CATEGORY   CM, MV, Short Movie

TEL / FAX   +81 (0)3 5712 5672
+81 (0)3 5712 5673

E-MAIL   tdg_info@d-guild.com
URL   http://www.d-guild.com/

3

4

Born in Kobe in 1973. Graduated from Waseda University and the Kuwasawa Design
School. In 1997 he started working in the producing and directing fields at Dentsu Tec.
In 2002 he took off work and went to Los Angeles for a year and a half. Upon returning to
Japan, he finished up at Dentsu Tec in April 2006. In May he joined THE DIRECTORS
GUILD. Focusing on the direction of tv commercials, he is involved in many areas
including short movies and music videos.

077

志賀匠
TAKUMI SHIGA

1981年生まれ。札幌デジタル専門学校デジタル映像科卒業。在学中からTV-CM、TV番組オープ
ニング CG、Station ID、MVなどを手がけ、現在はディレクター／CG作家として活動中。.mov
festival世界クリエイターズ100選ノミネート。2007年エジンバラ国際映画祭作品上映、2006年
RESFEST Japan Tour作品招待、shots作品掲載など。

1

2

1　MV – 二千花 Nichika, *Genius Party*
　　Director+CG: 志賀匠 Takumi Shiga, Camera:
　　小川ミキ Miki Ogawa, Light: 山盛修 Osamu
　　Yamamori, Producer: 上里滋 Shigeru Agari,
　　Production by P.I.C.S. (©R and C Ltd., 2007)

2　MV – 湧口愛美「炎の女」Aimi Yuguchi, *Honoo
　　no Onna* Director+CG: 志賀匠 Takumi Shiga
　　CG: 新田哲也 Tetsuya Nitta + 大澤龍一 Ryuichi

　　Osawa, Camera: 小川ミキ Miki Ogawa, Producer:
　　平賀大介 Daisuke Hiraga, Production by P.I.C.S.
　　(©Victor Entertainment, Inc. / SWEETSTAR LABEL,
　　2006)

3　CM – *Microsoft Office 2008 for Mac shotgun*
　　Director+CG: 志賀匠 Takumi Shiga, Producer:
　　小浜元 Hajime Kohama, A&P/MTV JAPAN+P.
　　I.C.S. (©MTV NETWORKS JAPAN, 2008)

4　MV – GO! GO! 7188「脳内トラベラー」
　　Nounai Traveller
　　Director+CG: 志賀匠 Takumi Shiga, Camera:
　　中原昌哉 Masaya Nakahara, Light: 山本剛
　　Tsuyoshi Yamamoto, Producer: 福田麻衣子
　　Maiko Fukuda, Production by SMC + OMB
　　(©BMG JAPAN Inc., 2007)

BELONG TO	P.I.C.S.management	CATEGORY	MV
TOOLS	LightWave, After Effects, Premiere Pro, Final Cut	TEL / FAX	+81 (0)3 5785 1780 +81 (0)3 5785 1784
		E-MAIL	post.mg@picsco.net
		URL	http://www.picsco.net

3

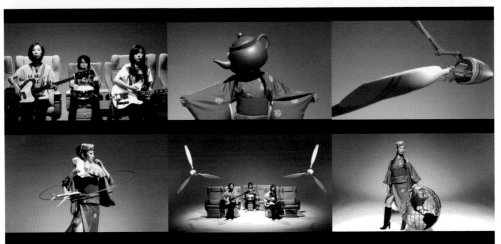

4

Born in 1981. Graduated from Sapporo Digital College, digital visual department. While at school, he was already making TV commercials, TV program opening, computer graphics, Station IDs and music videos. Currently, he works as a director/computer graphics creator (belongs to P.I.C.S. management), He was nominated as one of the 100 best creators at the DOTMOV FESTIVAL. His works was screened at the 2007 Edinburgh International Film Festival, he was invited to the 2006 RESFEST Japan Tour and has been featured in the magazine "shots".

078

島田大介
DAISUKE SHIMADA

Qotori film コトリフィルム代表 / SOUMA*走馬（AKEBOSHI＋島田大介＋松岡亮）メンバー。1974年大阪生まれ。京都芸術短期大学映像科卒業。松本俊夫氏、伊藤高志氏に実験映像を学び、その後ロンドンに遊学。その時に出会った写真家 Jean-Baptiste Mondino、映画監督 Tarsem Singh のものづくりに圧倒される。帰国後、谷田一郎率いる「John and Jane Doe Inc.」に入社。アシスタントディレクターを務めた後独立。MV、CM などを手がける。

1

2

| | MV – 10-FEET, *STONE COLD BREAK* (©BADASS / NAYUTAWAVE RECORDS, 2007) | 3 | MV – Kaela Kimura, *YELLOW* (©Columbia Music Entertainment Inc., 2007) |
| 2 | MV – 9mm Parabellum Bullet, *Discommunication* (©Capitol Music Co. / EMI Music Japan Inc., 2007) | 4 | MV – Yo Hioto, *Tadaima* (©Columbia Music Entertainment Inc., 2007) |

BELONG TO	コトリフィルム	CATEGORY	MV, CM, Movie,
	Qotori film		Animation
TOOLS	After Effects,	E-MAIL	info@qotori.com
	Final Cut	URL	http://www.qotori.com

3

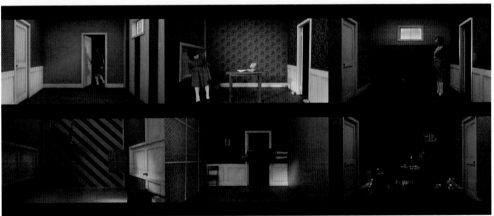

4

Repis entire od Qotri Film and member of Souma* member with AKEBOSHI and Ryo Matsuoka. Born in Osaka 1974, graduated from Kyoto College of Art, depertment of film. from Toshio Matsumoto and Takashi Ito, then moved to London and Influenced by Jean-Batiste Mordiao and Taisensigh's work. Afetre he returned to Japan, Assistant director at Ichiro Tanida (John and Jane Doe Inc.), now independent; videos, commercials, etc.

清水康彦
YASUHIKO SHIMIZU

1981年生まれ。2002年OMB Ltd.に参加し音楽映像を演出。2004年エジンバラ国際映画祭出展、
2006年RESFEST JAPAN/KOREA参加など、日本のみならず海外へも活動の幅を広げている。
2007年独立。

S

1

2

1	MV – DOPING PANDA, *nothin'* (gr8!records, 2008)	3	MV – monobright, 「未完成ライオット」 *Mikansei Riot* (Defstar Records, 2007)
2	MV – Hi-5, *ability* (EMI Music Japan, 2003)	4	MV – 日華 Nikka, *NO.1* (Far Eastern Tribe Records, 2008)

TOOLS   After Effects,
Final Cut,
Illustrator,
Photoshop,
Painter

CATEGORY   CM, MV, Web

E-MAIL   shimizu@tune.ocn.ne.jp
URL   http://shimizuyasuhiko.
blog74.fc2.com/

3

4

Born in 1981. In 2002 he started working at OMB Ltd. and directed motion graphics
for music. He is involved in a wide range of activities not only at Japan but also abroad,
including showing at the Edinburgh International Film Festival and the 2006 Japan/Korea
RESFEST. Went into business on his own in 2007.

080

新海岳人
TAKETO SHINKAI

1982年生まれ。愛知県立芸術大学卒。アニメとしての動きは最小限に抑え、会話でストーリーが展開する「会話劇アニメーション」の制作など、シナリオライティングをベースに置いた映像制作活動を行っている。第8回文化庁メディア芸術祭アニメーション部門奨励賞ほか受賞多数。また文筆家としての一面もあり、ブログ「うそ日記」は書籍化されている。

1

2

| 1 | Original – *Yama to Hito*
(©Taketo Shinkai, 2007) | 3 | Original – *Baito de Anime Jiyujin*
/ *Hero version*
(©Sugar Company / Jiyujin, 2007) |
| 2 | Original – *Moshimoshi*
(©Taketo Shinkai, 2007) | 4 | Original – *Yume*
(©Taketo Shinkai, 2004) |

TOOLS	After Effects, Final Cut	CATEGORY	Animation, MV, Short Movie
		TEL	090 4466 2283
		E-MAIL	taketoshinkai@yahoo.co.jp
		URL	http://taketoshinkai.com/

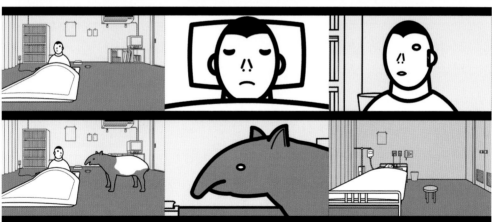

Born in 1982, Graduated from the Aichi Prefectural University of Fine Arts and Music. At minimize motions of animation. his motion graphic activities are based on screenwriting, He creates "conversation-based animation", the story is propelled forward through conversation. He recieved many awards, including the animation prize of 8th Japan Media Arts Festivals.

白川東一
MOTOHIRO SHIRAKAWA

081

1974年大阪生まれ。神戸芸術工科大学卒業後、1998年空気株式会社入社。現在に至る。主に2D、3Dアニメーションのディレクションを手がける。30代になり、子供もでき、随分と人生観が変わった中で今後どのような映像を生み出せるか。自分自身にかなり期待中。現在、オリジナルの短編アニメーションを制作中。

1 MV – ロボキャッチャー *Robo catcher*
  (MechaTracks Co.,ltd., 2007)

2 CM – 江戸しぐさ *Edo Shigusa*
  (ADKArts Inc., 2006)

3 Station ID – *HappySundays*
  (Animax Broadcast Japan Inc., 2006)

4 Opening Title – 実況パワフルメジャーリーグ2
  Jikkyou pawafuru Major League 2
  (Konami Digital Entertainment Co.,ltd.,
  2007)

BELONG TO	空気株式会社 KOO-KI CO.,LTD.	CATEGORY	Opening Title, Short Movie, Animation
TOOLS	After Effects, Illustrator, Photoshop	TEL / FAX	+81 (0)92 874 2020 +81 (0)92 874 2010
		E-MAIL URL	shira@koo-ki.co.jp http://www.koo-ki. co.jp

3

4

Born in Osaka in 1974. Graduated from Kobe Design University and joined KOO-KI in 1998. Involved mainly in the direction of 2-D and 3-D animation. On becoming a father in his 30's, his outlook on life changed, making one wonder if his visual imagination will also be influenced. He himself is really looking forward to it. He is now producing an animation short.

082

ソライロ
SORAIRO

オムニバス・ジャパンを経て、2005年から映像制作ユニット「ソライロ」として活動。CM、MVなどのCG、エフェクトを演出・制作する傍ら、オリジナル作品にも精力的に取り組んでいる。

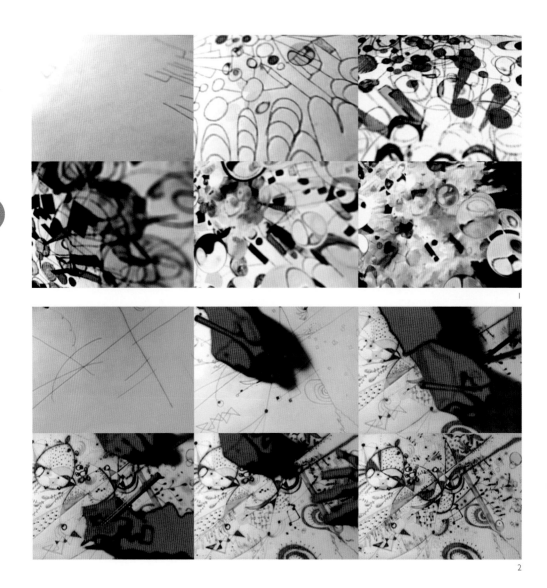

S

1

2

1	Original Work – *horizon*	3	Original Work – *alchemy*
	(©Sorairo, 2006)		(©Sorairo, 2008)
2	Original Work – *drawing*	4	Original Work – *reel06*
	(©Sorairo, 2008)		(©Sorairo, 2008)

TOOLS	Maya, 3ds Max, Photoshop, Illustrator, After Effects, Premiere	CATEGORY	CM, MV, Short Movie, Animation
		TEL / FAX	+81 (0)3 6801 7850 +81 (0)3 6801 7850
		E-MAIL URL	info@sorairo-web.com http://blog.sorairo-web.com/

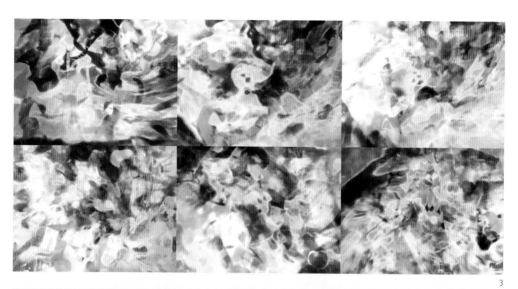

3

4

After working at Omnibus Japan, began activities as the unit "Sorairo" in 2005. While focusing mainly on the production and direction of effects and the CG for commercials and music videos, they are also tirelessly at work on their own projects.

083

菅原そうた
SOTA SUGAHARA

1979年8月16日生まれ。CG作品の中に潜む狂気と笑いをタナカカツキ氏に見いだされ「バカCG」
作家として開花。漫画家、VJ、CG作家、プロモーションビデオディレクター、アニメディレクター、
映画監督。キャラクターデザインもこなす。

1

2

3

4

1　Baka CG - 「あいうえお」*aiueo* (Tonio Pro, 2007)	3　Mobile Movie - 「サイケデリック」 *Psychedelic* (NTT DoCoMo, Inc., 2007)

5　MV - 「トニブリック」*Toni Brick*
(Tonio Pro+MEDICOM TOY CORPORATION.,
2007)

2　Short Movie - 「ネットミラクルショッピング」
Net Miracle Shopping
(©Production Committee, 2008)

4　Baka CG - 「キモちゃん」*Kimo-chan*
(Tonio Pro, 2008)

6　DVD - 関根勤「妄想力」
Tsutomu Sekine, MousouRyoku
(PONY CANYON INC., 2008)

TOOLS	Poser, After Effects, Photoshop	CATEGORY	MV, CM, Short Movie, Baka CG
		E-MAIL	sota@suga.gr.jp

5

6

Born on August 16th, 1979. He blossomed as a creator when the madness and laughter hidden within his works were discovered by Katsuki Tanaka who called them "silly CG". Comic artist, CG creator, promotional video director, animation director, movie director. Also involved in character design.

084

須藤カンジ
KANJI SUTO

1974年神奈川生まれ。大学、3DCGの専門学校を卒業後、1999年よりゲーム、番組オープニングタイトルなどのCGやグラフィックデザイン・制作・演出を開始。2002年より、丹修一氏に師事しMVに携わる。以降2004年にディレクターとして独立し、フリーランスのディレクターとして数々のMV、CMなどを手がける。

1

2

1	MV – RIZE, *LADY LOVE* (UNIVERSAL MUSIC KK., 2007)	3	MV – CHEMISTRY, *almost in love* (Defstar Records Inc., 2005)
2	MV – RADWIMPS「セツナレンサ」 *Setsunarensa* (EMI Music Japan Inc., 2006)	4	MV – SHAKALABBITS, *MutRon* (XLQ Corporation, 2007)

TOOLS	After Effects,	CATEGORY	MV, Art Movie,
	Final Cut		CG Animation, CM
	SOFTIMAGE XSI,		
	Photoshop,	TEL / FAX	+81 (0)3 3320 7477
	Illustrator		+81 (0)3 3320 7477
		E-MAIL	kanji@co.email.ne.jp

3

4

Born in Kanagawa in 1974. After specializing in 3-D CG in university and professional school, in 1999 he began production and direction of things like CG and graphic design for games, program openings, opening titles, etc. Became involved in music videos under the tutelage of Shuichi Tan. A freelance director since 2004, he has been involved in many music videos and commercials.

085

高木正勝
TAKAGI MASAKATSU

1979年生まれ、京都府在住。映像と音楽両方の制作を等価に手がけ、双方の質の高い融合により注目を集めるアーティスト。国内外のレーベルからCD／DVDをリリースすると同時に、アート・スペースでの展覧会や世界各地でのライブなど、分野に限定されない多様な活動を展開。デヴィッド・シルヴィアンのワールド・ツアーへの参加、UAやYUKIのミュージックビデオ制作、ダンスや映画、CM音楽の制作なども行っている。ワシントンDCで開催された日本フェスティバル「JAPAN! Culture+Hyperculture」に出演するなど、海外での評価も高い。

1

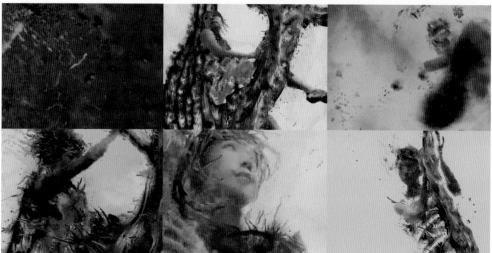

2

| | 1 | Original Work – *Tidal* (sound and visual by Takagi Masakatsu, 2007) | 3 | Original Work – *Philharmony* (sound and visual by Takagi Masakatsu, 2007) |

1　Original Work – *Tidal* (sound and visual by Takagi Masakatsu, 2007)

3　Original Work – *Philharmony* (sound and visual by Takagi Masakatsu, 2007)

2　MV – *Seamless* (music by Sandy Lam, visual by Takagi Masakatsu, 2007)

4　Original Work – *Lava* (sound and visual by Takagi Masakatsu, 2008)

BELONG TO	エピファニーワークス Epiphany Works	CATEGORY	Art, Installation, MV
		TEL / FAX	+81 (0)3 3448 0745 +81 (0)3 3448 0745
TOOLS	After Effects, Final Cut		
		E-MAIL	info@epiphanyworks.net
		URL	http://www. takagimasakatsu.com http://www. epiphanyworks.net

3

4

Born 1979, lives in Kyoto. Produces both quality images and music, is released
internationally on CD and DVD, and exhibits and performs live worldwide. Was involved
in David Sylvain's world tour, has produced music videos for the likes of UA and
Yuki, and has made dance movies and music for commercials. Participation in "Japan!
Culture+Hyperculture" in Washington D. C. added to his reputation.

086

タナカカツキ
KATSUKI TANAKA

1966年大阪生まれ。1985年マンガ家としてデビュー。著書に「バカドリル」「オッス！トン子ちゃん」
（扶桑社）などがある。

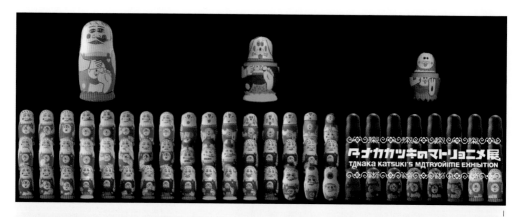

1

2

1　Exhibition –「タナカカツキのマトリョニメ展」
　　Tanaka Katsuki no Matoryonime
　　(gallery ask?, 2007)

2　Exhibition –
　　「タナカカツキの顔ハメ☆パノラ－－－マ！展」
　　Tanaka Katsuki no Kao-hame panorama!
　　(Olympus Corporation, 2007)

3　Exhibition –「タナカカツキの太郎ビーム！展」
　　Tanaka Katsuki no Taro Beam!
　　(Taro Okamoto Memorial Museum, 2007)

4　Exhibition – 文化庁メディア芸術祭／
　　日本の表現力「イエス☆パノラーマ」360°
　　Tanaka Katsuki no YES panorama! (2007)

CATEGORY   Exhibition, MV
                Short Animation

E-MAIL   ka2ki@kaerucafe.com
URL   http://kaerucafe.com/

3

4

Born in Osaka in 1966. Made his debut as a comic artist in 1985. Author of, among other works, "Bakadoriru" and "Ossu! Tonko-chan" (Publ. Fusosha).

087 田中賢一郎
KENICHIRO TANAKA

1969年熊本生まれ。土木系コンサルタント、㈱ビデオステーションキューを経て2003年空気株式会社入社。主に、TV-CM、映画におけるCGIディレクション、制作、コンサルティングおよびエフェクト開発を手がける。実写をモチーフにした自然な画作りを得意とするほか、柔軟なアプローチで独創的な作風を目指す。最近では「蟲師」「ゲゲゲの鬼太郎」「監督バンザイ」などのVFXに参加。

1

2

I	CM – ソラリアプラザ「アリダンス篇」 SOLARIA PLAZA, *Ant Dance* (SOLARIA PLAZA, 2003)	3	CM – JJ自由時間「マリオネット篇」 JJ Jiyujikan, *Marionette* (JJ Jiyujikan, 2006)
2	CM – フンドーキン「ライオンとうさぎ篇」 fundokin, *Lion and rabbit* (fundokin, 2003)	4	Game Movie – *wccf 2006-2007* (SEGA, 2007)

BELONG TO	空気株式会社	CATEGORY	CM, Movie, MV,
	KOO-KI CO.,LTD.		Game Movie
TOOLS	Maya/MEL,	TEL / FAX	+81 (0)92 874 2020
	Shake,		+81 (0)92 874 2010
	C/C++,		
	OpenGL	E-MAIL	mom@koo-ki.co.jp
		URL	http://www.koo-ki.
			co.jp

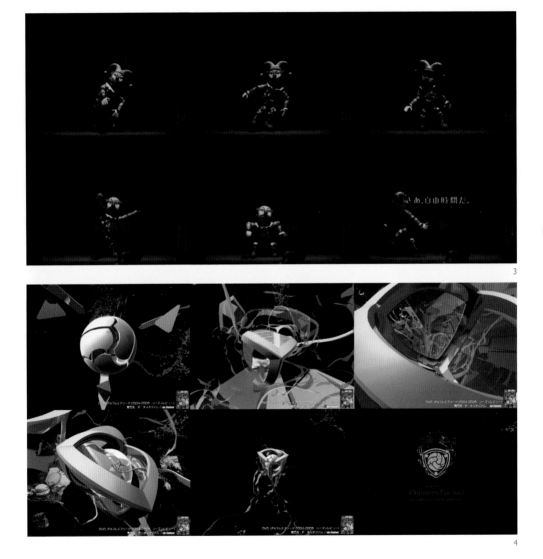

3

4

Born 1969, Kumamoto. A civil engineering consultant, worked on Video station Q, joined Koo-Ki in 2003. Producing and directing mostly commercials and movie CGI, also involved in consulting and effect development. Best at natural live action images, also aspires to inventive and flexible methods. Recently involved in the "MUSHISHI", "GeGeGe no Kitaro", and "Glory to the Filmmaker!" video effects.

088

田中裕介
YUSUKE TANAKA

1978年生まれ。多摩美術大学グラフィックデザイン科卒業。卒業後、株式会社ピラミッドフィルム入社。Tera monkeysに所属。2007年に独立し、CAVIARに参加する。

1

2

	MV – Vidal Sassoon Collaboration Video 安室奈美恵 Namie Amuro, *ROCK STEADY* (P&G, avex, 2008)	3	CM – マックフルーリー 「キャラメル & オレオが出来るまで篇」 *mcflurry "Caramel & Oreo ga Dekirumade"* (Mcdonald's Holdings Company (Japan), Ltd., 2007)
2.	MV – AYUSE KOZUE, *SANDAE LOVE* (TOY'S FACTORY, 2007)	4	ShortMovie – *Gillette Fusion 5+1* 「快感篇」*Kaikan-Hen* (P&G, 2007)

BELONG TO	キャビア Caviar Limited	CATEGORY	MV, CM, Short Movie, Animation, Motion Graphics
TOOLS	After Effects, Final Cut, CINEMA 4D, 3ds Max, Shake		
		TEL / FAX	+81 (0)3 3791 9300 +81 (0)3 3791 9310
		E-MAIL URL	meetme@caviar.ws http://www.caviar.ws

3

4

Born in 1978. Graduated from Tama Art University with a degree in graphic design. After graduation he started working at Pyramid Film Inc. Affiliated with "Tera Monkeys". He became freelance in 2007 and is also a member of Caviar.

089

タムデム
TAMDEM

CAVIARのタムカイジュン（tam）とデムラタクヤ（dem）により2007年に結成。イベントのVJなど から活動を始める。主にモーショングラフィックスを得意とする映像制作ユニットであり、木村カ エラ「jasper」のMVにCGで参加するなど、CAVIAR所属監督のCG制作にも携わる。

I

2

1　MV – KAN TAKAGI, *T.I.M.E*
　　feat. ANI・BOSE(Scha Dara Parr),
　　VERBAL(m-flo) and LUPE FIASCO
　　"G-SHOCK 25th Anniversary ORIGINAL TRACK"
　　(©CASIO COMPUTER CO., LTD., 2007)

2　TV – SPACE SHOWER TV, *ZAMURAI TV*
　　HIFANA featuring IZUPON
　　(©SPACE SHOWER NETWORK, 2007)

3　VJ – TOWA TEI, *EVENT MOTIVATION*

BELONG TO	**タムデム** tamdem	CATEGORY	MV, CM, Short Movie, Animation, Motion Graphics
TOOLS	After Effects, Final Cut, CINEMA 4D Painter	TEL / FAX	+81 (0)3 3791 9300 +81 (0)3 3791 9310
		E-MAIL URL	meetme@caviar.ws http://www.caviar.ws

3

4

4   Opening Title –
    ANIMAX「年末年始がおもしろい1週間」
    Nenmatsu Nenshi ga Omoshiroi 1 Shuukan
    (©Animax Broadcast Japan Inc., 2007)

In 2007 CAVIAR's Jun Tamukai ("tam") and Takuya Demura ("dem") founded
Tamdem. They began their activities which include VJing at events. Forming a
unit whose main specialty is motion graphics, they have been involved in the
CG for Kaela Kimura ("Jasper")'s music videos and in the creation of CG for
CAVIAR directors.

090

TANGE FILMS

2006年設立。森下征治と丹羽直樹のユニットによるTANGE FILMSはマンガ・音楽・ファッション・グラフィックデザイン・アートなどの様々なエレメンツとアニメーションをグローバルミックスし、高純度なグラフィックへと昇華させることことで生まれる、スタイリッシュなビジュアルインパクトの創造を目的とする。見た者の感情に強い「快感」と「余韻」を与えるビジュアルを世界に向けて発信していく。

1

2

I	Short Movie – *AKARUI-MUSYOKU* (©Hiroshi Okuda)	3 Opening Movie – *Brillia ShortShorts Theater* (©Visual Voice./TANGE FILMS) Music: Taro Ishida
2	Logo Animation – *BI COLOR* (©Junya Shigematsu) Art Direction: Junya Shigematsu Music: Tatsuya Yamada flowt.jp	4 Prohibition Matter Introduction – *Brillia ShortShorts Theater* (©Visual Voice./TANGE FILMS) Music: Taro Ishida

TOOLS	After Effcts, Final Cut, SOFTIMAGE XSI, Photoshop, Illustrator	CATEGORY	MV, CM, Short Movie, Animation, Illustration
		TEL	+81 (0)3 3807 7123
		E-MAIL	info@tangefilms.jp
		URL	http://www.tangefilms.jp/ http://www.lftlabel.com/

3

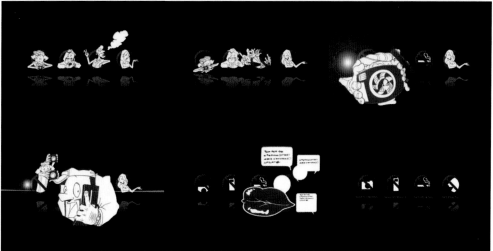

4

Seiji Morishita and Naoki Niwa's unit makes a global mix, blending animation with various elements like comics, music, fashion, graphic design and art. They aim at pure graphics and stylish visual impact born from sublimation, and will proceed to transmit visuals that provide the viewer with intense pleasure and afterglow.

091

谷篤
ATSUSHI TANI

1974年生まれ。武蔵野美術大学建築学科卒業。2001年より teevee graphics に参加。MV、CM、ブロードキャストデザインなどの企画・演出からモーショングラフィックス制作まで、ジャンルを超えて精力的に活動中。

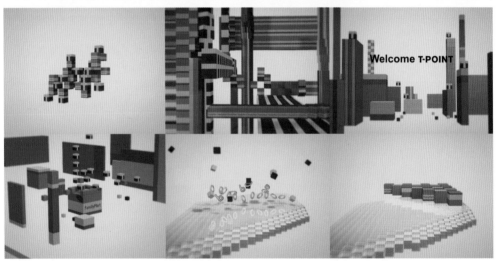

1　MV - キリンジ「朝焼けは雨のきざし」
　　Kirinji, *Asayake Ha Ame No Kizashi*
　　(©Columbia Music Entertainment, 2008)

2　CM - ファミリーマート Family Mart, *Welcom
　　T-POINT* (2007)

3　Station ID - MUSIC ON! TV,
　　X'mas ID (2007)

4　Broadcast Design - 日本テレビ「爆笑問題のナ
　　ニゲに凄～い超人劇場」 Nippon Television
　　Network Corporation, *Bakushoumondai
　　no Nanigeni Sugoi Cyoujin Gekijou* (2008)

BELONG TO	ティ・ビィ・グラフィックス teevee graphics	CATEGORY	MV, CM, Broadcast Design, Station ID
TOOLS	After Effects, LightWave, Photoshop, Illustrator, Combustion	TEL / FAX	+81 (0)3 3400 6455 +81 (0)3 5468 7048
		E-MAIL URL	tani@teeveeg.com http://www.teeveeg. com

3

4

Born in 1974. Graduated from the department of architecture at Musashino Art
University and joined teevee graphics in 2001. Surpassing genre, he works tirelessly on
everything from the production and direction of music videos, commercials and broadcast
design, to the execution of motion graphics.

092

丹治まさみ
MASAMI TANZI

1972年生まれ。武蔵野美術大学日本画学科卒業後、Webデザイン会社を経てフリーランスで3DCG
を始める。2007年、DVDアニメーション「茄子 スーツケースの渡り鳥」CG監督。3DCGの存在意
義を確認するかのようなプリミティブな美しさを持った映像がコンセプト。講師業、映像や静止画、
インタラクティブな作品制作まで幅広く活動中。「デジタル映像制作ガイドブック」をはじめ、執筆
書も多数。

1

2

I	Short Movie – *Tower of bebel* (2002)	3	MV – 戸田誠司 Seiji Toda, *memory* (NOWONMEDIA, INC., 2005)
2	Short Movie – *blidge* (2004)	4	Other Works その他の作品 (2002-2008)

| TOOLS | After Effects, LightWave | CATEGORY | MV, CM, Short Movie, Animation |
| | | E-MAIL | masami@tanzi.jp |

3

4

Born in 1972. Musashino Art University Japanese Painting degree. After web design company, then freelance 3-D CG. In 2007 directed CG for the DVD animation "Nasu Sutsukesu No Wataridori". Concept: "primitive beauty confirming the importance of existence". Various activities include teaching, motion graphics, stop motion and interactive works. Wrote a guide book to digital motion graphic creation.

093

田尾創樹
SOJU TAO

1977年生まれ。大学を経済的な困難により中退、2年ほど途方に暮れる。その後オカメプロ（現在はおかめぶろ）に入社。雑務、営業の合間をぬい社内広報映像、CM及び所属アーティストのMVなどを手がける。2006年5月YOUTUBEに初めてビデオをアップロードする。

1

2

1	MV – Okamehachimoku, *Shirasagi-kun* (OkamePro, 2006)	3	MV – Perfectdancer, *Shigemitsu* (OkamePro, 2007)
2	MV– Perfectdancer, *Jada Hey Ho* (OkamePro, 2007)	4	MV – Perfectdancer feart. Tazumayama, *Thank you* (OkamePro, 2006)

BELONG TO	おかめぷろ OkamePro	CATEGORY	MV, CM, Short Movie, Animation
TOOLS	Windows Movie Maker, iMovie HD	E-MAIL	okamepro@hotmail. co.jp
		URL	http://plaza. rakuten.co.jp/ okamehachimoku/

Born in 1977. Quitting university because of economic hardship, for two years he was at a loss for what to do. Then he started working at Okame Pro. Using the time between his miscellaneous duties, he works on the company's internal video bulletins, commercials and the music videos of affiliated artists. He uploaded his first video to YouTube in May 2006.

094

辻川幸一郎
KOICHIRO TSUJIKAWA

1972年生まれ。1993年よりデザイナーとしてレコードジャケットなどを手がける。ある時友人のコーネリアスに誘われて、独学でライブ用の映像を制作し始める。以後いつの間にかフリーのディレクターとして、MVやCMなど様々な分野の仕事に携わるようになる。

1

2

1　MV – Cornelius, *Omstart*
　(©WARNER MUSIC JAPAN INC., 2007)

2　MV – Cornelius, *Fit Song*
　(©WARNER MUSIC JAPAN INC., 2007)

3　Short Movie – *Kimagure Robot*
　(©NTT DoCoMo, Kadokawa Mobile, inc.,
　Kadokawa the Television Co.,LTD., ASMIK
　ACE ENTERTAINMENT, INC., 2007)

4　MV – Cornelius, *Like a Rolling Stone*
　(©WARNER MUSIC JAPAN INC., 2007)

TOOLS	After Effects	CATEGORY	CM, MV, Short Movie, ID, Logo Design
		TEL / FAX	+81 (0)3 6427 1633 +81 (0)3 6427 1633
		E-MAIL URL	jick01@mac.com http://www. tsujikawakoichiro.com

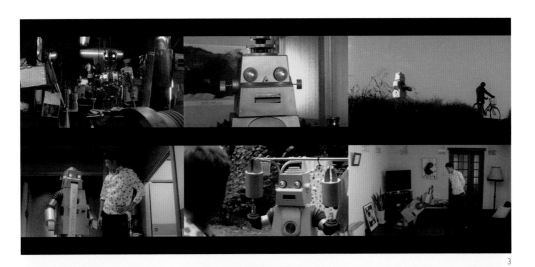

3

4

Born in 1972. Began his activities as a designer in 1993 with record jackets and the like. He began his self taught creation of motion graphics for live shows upon the invitation of his friend Cornelius. Before he knew it, he was working every day as a freelance director in a variety of fields including promotional videos and TV commercials.

095

上田大樹
TAIKI UEDA

1978年生まれ。早稲田大学中退。在学中より、劇団の主宰を経て、映像制作を始める。instant wife 代表。NLYON100° C、大人計画、劇団☆新感線などの劇中映像や、MV および CM のディレクション、TV や映画のタイトルバック、CHANEL銀座ビルのファサードアニメーション、LIVE の演出映像、ショートフィルム、グラフィックデザインなどを手がける。第25回ぴあフィルムフェスティバルでグランプリを受賞。現在、モーショングラフィックスから実写映像制作に移行中。

	LIVE - Mr.children "home" tour	3	Short film - カミロボ「居酒屋ブルーキラー」
	「シーソーゲーム」 Seesaw Game		Kami Robo, Izakaya Blues Killer
	(©Oorong-sha Co Ltd., 2007)		(©Butterfly-stroke.inc, 2006)
2	Tittle Movie - 「'Ns' あおい」	4	Movie in Play -
	N's Aoi		阿佐ヶ谷スパイダース「少女とガソリン」
	(©Fuji Television Network, Inc., 2006)		Asagaya Spiders, Shojo to Gasoline
			(©Gorch Brothers, 2007)

BELONG TO	インスタントワイフ	CATEGORY	MV, Short Movie,
	instant wife		Animation
TOOLS	After Effects,	E-MAIL	info@instantwife.com
	Final Cut,	URL	http://instantwife.com
	Photoshop,		
	Illustrator,		
	Motion,		
	ArkaosVJ,		
	Projector		

2

3

4

Born 1978. Dropped out of Waseda University. At school, head of a theatre group, made motion graphics. "instant wife" president. Makes footage for theatre groups NYLON 100°C, Otona Keikaku, Gekidan Shinkansen; music videos, commercials, direction; TV, movies, title backgrounds; CHANEL Ginza, animated façade, live visuals, short films, and graphic design. 25th Pia Film Festival Grand Prize. Now moving from motion graphics to live action.

096

宇川直宏
NAOHIRO UKAWA

1968年生まれ。デザイナー、VJ、ビデオディレクター、映画監督、文筆家、京都造形芸術大学教授、パンクスなど、ジャンルを超越してメディアをジャックする全方位クリエイター。

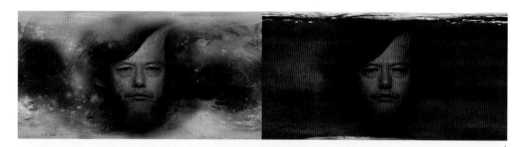

1

2

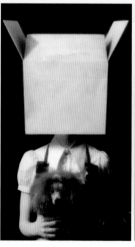

3

1　DVD, MV - 板尾創路「少年B」
　Itao Itsuji, *Shonen B*
　(©2008 YOSHIMOTO R&C)

2　DVD, MV - 板尾創路「太陽を盗んだ少年 B」
　Itao Itsuji, *Taiyo wo Nusunda Shonen B*
　(©2008 YOSHIMOTO R&C)

3　Web-CM - Laforet HARAJUKU Online Store,
　UNDERGROUND
　(©Laforet HARAJUKU, Ukawa Naohiro, 2008)

4　DVD - *INTOXICATING MUSIC CLIPS OF
　UKAWA NAOHIRO "MAD HAT LAUGHS!!!!!"*
　(©Ki/oon Records, Sony Music
　Entertainment, 2007)

BELONG TO	Mixrooffice, GODFATHER Yamamoto Gendai, MOM'N'DAD PRODUCTIONS, KYOTO ZOUKEI UNIVERSITY, JAPAN SOCIETY FOR NATURAL DISASTER SCIENCE	CATEGORY	VJ, Art, MV
		E-MAIL	video@ukawa.tv
		URL	http://www.ukawa.tv/
TOOLS	AMIGA VIDEO TOASTER, CommodoreVIC-20, APPLE Macintosh SE30		

Born in 1968. Ukawa is a designer, VJ, video director, movie director, writer, a professor at Kyoto University Of Arts And Design and an omnidirectional creator who transcends genre (e.g. punk) and hijacks the media.

097

ワウラブ
WOWLAB

WOW仙台のスタッフを中心に、インターフェイスとしての映像を研究するためにスタートしたデザインユニット。感性と技術の融合、そしてデザインと開発の一体化を目指す。インターフェイスデザイン、インスタレーションの展示、モーショングラフィックスなど、幅広い表現活動を展開。

1

2

1	Installation – *Light Rain*	3	Original Work – *New Moon*
2	Installation – *Tengible*	4	Installation – *Motion Texture*

BELONG TO	ワウ WOW	CATEGORY	Media Art, Interface Design, Motion Graphics, Visual Effect
TOOLS	CINEMA 4D, After Effects, Processing, Quartz Composer	E-MAIL URL	info@wowlab.net http://www.wowlab.net/

3

4

**Art Center College Library
1700 Lida St.
Pasadena, CA 91103**

A design unit with its main staff in Sendai, begun for the purpose of researching motion graphics as interface. Aims to blend aesthetic sensibility and technique, integrating them with development in design. Their expressive activities span a broad range, including interface design, installation exhibition, and motion graphics.

098

耶雲哉治
SAIJI YAKUMO

1976年生まれ。早稲田大学卒業。在学中に自主映画を制作。1998年 東京学生映画祭グランプリ、2000年 JCF学生映画祭グランプリ。2000年からROBOTに所属しTV-CMの演出を始め、2003年第41回ギャラクシー賞奨励賞受賞。さらに、ドラマ、ドキュメンタリー、グラビアなどの演出。最近は自ら撮影することも多い。

1
2
3
4
5
6
7
8
8
9
10
11

1 CM - 東京オリンピック招致委員会「みのさん語る」 Minosan Kataru (TOKYO 2016 Olympic Games Bid Committee., 2007)
2 CM - ボシュロム・ジャパン「Medalist II」(B.L.J. Company, Ltd., 2005)
3 CM - 読売新聞「文芸小説 PR」Bungei Shousetsu PR (The Yomiuri Shimbun 2003)
4 CM - Warner Home Video, O.C (Waner Bros. Entertainment Inc., 2007)
5 CM - Mos Burger「パオチキン」Pao chicken (Mos Food Services, Inc., 2005)

6 CM - ヒューマンアカデミー「Human Academy」 (Human Academy Co., Ltd 2006)
7 CM - Pony Canyon「Re:Genesis」 (Pony Canyon Inc., 2007)
8 CM - 第一興商「BIG ECHO」 (Daiichikosho Co.,Ltd. 2007)
9 CM - コレステロール甘く見ない!!! キャンペーン Cholesterol Amaku Minai!!! Campaign (ASTELLAS PHARMA Inc. / PFIZER Japan Inc., 2007)
10 CM - H.I.S「初夢フェア 2008」Hatsuyume Fair (H.I.S.Co.,Ltd., 2008)

11 CM - ユニ・チャーム ペットケア「銀のスプーン」Gin no Spoon (Unicharm Co..Ltd., 2007)
12 DVD - 「2U SKI の神様と日々の記録 2 編」Aiko Uemura 2004-2006 2U SKI no Kamisama to Hibi no Kiroku "Aiko Uemura 2004-2006" (©SPORTS BIZ/ROBOT/Excite, 2006)
13 Original Works - 「おっぱいプリン」Oppai Pudding (2003, 2005)
14 DVD - エースコック「スーパー DVD カップ」Super DVD Cup (ACE COOK CO.,Ltd., 2004)

BELONG TO   **ロボット**
             ROBOT

CATEGORY   **CM, MV, Drama,**
                   Documentary Film

TEL / FAX   **+81 (0)3 3760 1064**
                  +81 (0)3 3760 1347

E-MAIL   **yakumo@robot.co.jp**
URL   **http://www.robot.co.jp**

12

13

14

Born in 1976, Waseda University degree, began making own movies at school. Won the
Grand Prize at the 1998 Tokyo Student Film Festival and the Grand Prize at the 2000
JCF Student Film Festival. In 2000 joined Robot, began making TV commercials. In 2003
he won the 41st Galaxy Encouragement Prize. TV drama, documentary, and bikini model
video director. Recently doing more and more of the shooting himself.

099

山口崇司
TAKASHIYAMAGUCHI

1976年生まれ。映像作家・ビジュアルアーティスト。ゲーム会社、立花ハジメデザインでの勤務を経て独立。プログラミングを絡めた映像、メディアアート制作を主体とし、SiggraphなどでのCG作品入選、六本木クロッシング2007への参加など、国内外で活動。2006年よりItoken + Jimanicaのドラムデュオ＋インタラクティブ映像の変則トリオd.v.d（http://www.dvd-3.com/）を始動。ファーストDVD+CD『01>01』をリリース。

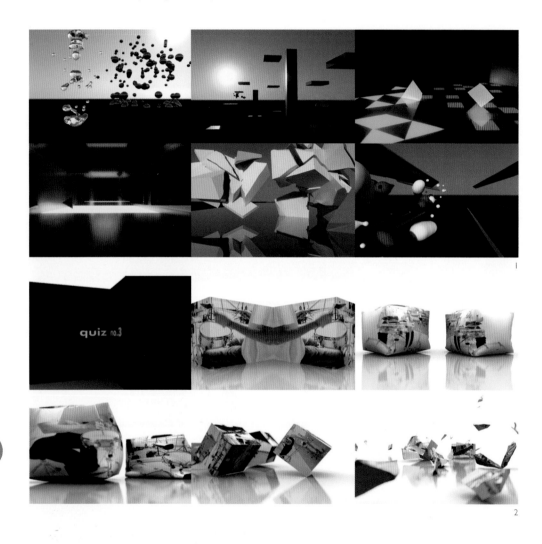

1

2

1　MV - d.v.d, *seek the planet no.8*
　　(HEADZ, 2007)

2　MV - d.v.d, *quiz no.3* (HEADZ, 2007)

3　Exhibition Movie - Planetarium MEGASTAR-
　　II cosmos「偶然の惑星」*Guuzen no Wakusei*
　　(National Museum of Emerging Science and
　　Innovation, 2007)

4　Web - pen-web, *LONDON* (pen, 2008)

		CATEGORY	MV, CM, ShortMovie,
BELONG TO	d.v.d		Animation, ArtInstallation,
			LiveInstallation
TOOLS	Maya,		
	After Effects,		
	Flash,	TEL / FAX	+81 (0)3 3794 4297
	Director,		+81 (0)3 3794 4297
	Processing,		
	Java,	E-MAIL	mail@takashiyamaguchi.com
	etc...	URL	http://www.takashiyamaguchi.com/
			http://www.dvd-3.com/

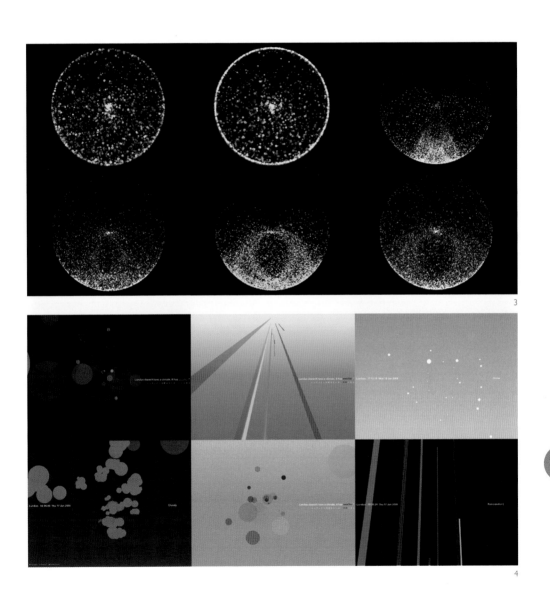

3

4

Born in 1976. Motion graphic creator and visual artist. Worked at a game company and Tachibana Hajime Design. Now freelance, focusing on image creation with programming and media art production, his CG work has won at Siggraph etc, and he showed at Roppongi Crossing 2007. In 2006 he started a trio with Itoken and Jimanica called "d.v.d." (http://www.dvd-3.com/). Their first DVD + CD is "01>01".

100

吉浦康裕
YASUHIRO YOSHIURA

1980年生まれ。九州芸術工科大学（現在は九州大学芸術工学部）にて芸術工学を専攻。2003年3月、同大学を卒業。大学時代にアニメーション制作を開始。卒業後はフリーでショートアニメーション制作を請け負い、2006年1月に、初のDVD作品『ペイル・コクーン』を発売。現在はシリーズ作品となる「イヴの時間」を制作中。

1

2

1　Animation – キクマナ *kikumana* (©Yasuhiro YOSHIURA, 2001)

2　Animation – 水のコトバ *Aquatic Lnguage* (©Yasuhiro YOSHIURA / DIRECTIONS, INC., 2003)

3　Animation – ペイル・コクーン *PALE COCOON* (©Yasuhiro YOSHIURA / DIRECTIONS, INC., 2005)

4　Animation – イヴの時間 *The Time of EVE* (©Yasuhiro YOSHIURA / DIRECTIONS, INC. 2008)

BELONG TO	スタジオ六花 Studio RIKKA	CATEGORY	MV, CM, Broadcast Design, Station ID
TOOLS	3ds Max, After Effects	TEL / FAX	+81 (0)3 5790 5111 +81 (0)3 5790 5112
		E-MAIL URL	info@studio-rikka.com http://www.studio- rikka.com/

3

4

Born in 1980. Graduated from the Kyushu Institute of Design in March 2003 with a degree in Arts and Crafts. Began working on animation and submitting to contests while still at school. Following graduation, he worked freelance on animation shorts and then released the first DVD collection of his work "Pale Cocoon" in January 2006. He is presently working on a series of works called "The Time of Eve".

映像作家
ワークプロファイル

CREATORS'
WORK PROFILES

236-255

映像作家100人 2008
ワークプロファイル

001　阿部 伸吾　ABE SHINGO

2005	CI - 「GAGA USEN」
2006	上映 - 「Nippon Koma」Pequeno Auditorio/ Lisboa, Portugal
2006	CI - 「WOWOW 15th」
2006	入賞 - RESFEST 2006
2007	CI - Yakult
2007	入賞 - 「Promax&BDA World Gold Award」 Art Direction & Design: Interstitial Campaign
2008	MV-THE JETZEJOHNSON「Dancetek」 （KING RECODS）
2008	CM - 「YAMAHA AT」

002　AC部　AC-BU

2000	受賞 - 「ユーロボーイズ」 デジスタアウォード 2000 グランプリ
2001	Short Movie - Sma STATION!! 「スマアニメ／カッコいい男たち篇」
2003	Short Movie - 「ロイヤルドラゴン」
2003	MV - みんなのうた「哲学するマントヒヒ」
2005	MV - ザマギ「マジカルDEATH」
2007	TV - 天才テレビくん BIT WORLD「BIT RACER」
2007	Short Movie - 星新一ショートショート劇場「プレゼント」
2007	TV - SMAP×SMAPブリッジ映像 「カラフルアラビアンナイト篇」

003　天久聖一　MASAKAZU AMAHISA

2003	Short Movie - 「悲しみジョニー」
2004	MV - 電気グルーヴ「カフェ・ド・鬼」（アニメ担当） SPACE SHOWER TV MUSIC VIDEO AWARDS BEST GROOVE VIDEO受賞
2004	MV - 電気グルーヴ「弾けないギターを弾くんだぜ」 （アニメ担当）
2007	MV - ゆらゆら帝国「美しい」（アニメ担当） SPACE SHOWER TV MUSIC VIDEO AWARDS

	BEST CG/ANIMATION VIDEO受賞
2008	MV - 電気グルーヴ「モノノケダンス」

004　アミカ　AMICA

2006	入賞 - 2006 アジアデジタルアート大賞
2006	受賞 - 第5回インディーズアニメフェスタ 三鷹賞 （グランプリ）・杉井賞
2006	受賞 - Digital Creators Competition 2006 金の 翼賞（グランプリ）
2006	受賞 -文化庁メディア芸術祭アニメーション部門 優秀賞
2007	受賞 - デジスタ・アウォード 2007 グランプリ
2007	入賞 - プラットフォーム国際映画祭
2007	入賞 - シュトゥットゥガルト国際映画祭 2007
2007	入賞 - タンペレ国際映画祭 2007

005　アンテナ　ANTENNA

2006	上映 - RESFEST10 Japana & Korea Tour RESMIX ELECTRONICA - 日本/韓国
2006	MV - RAM RIDER「HELLO」- 8bit edition （rhythmzone）Director: 田中英行
2006	MV - 荘野ジュリ「笑いたかった」（Victor Entertainment）Director: 田中英行
2006	受賞 - 第2回現代美術コンクール大賞受賞
2006	展覧会 - 「取手アートプロジェクト 06」出品 - 茨城
2007	展覧会 - 「National Highway No.1」出品 - 京幾道 美術館/韓国
2007	展覧会 - 「Videonale11」出品 - ボン美術館/ドイツ
2007	展覧会 - 「第10回岡本太郎現代芸術賞」出品 - 川崎 市岡本太郎美術館/神奈川

006　新井風愉　FUYU ARAI

1999	実験映像 - 「DOTS」
2000	実験映像 - 「play」
2001	受賞 - キャノンデジタルクリエーターズコンテスト ムービー部門グランプリ、ベネトンジャパン賞

2002	受賞 - キャノンデジタルクリエーターズコンテスト ムービー部門ブロンズ賞	
2002	上映 - Cinema de demain - ポンピドゥーセンター	
2003	映画予告 -「KILL BILL」特報第2段、TVCM	
2004	上映 - クレルモンフェラン国際短編映画祭 - フランス・オーベルニュ	
2007	CM - PASMO「あの街もこの街も篇」	

007　キャドセンター
CAD CENTER CORPORATION

1987～	大規模ビル・マンション（六本木ヒルズ、芝浦アイランド、The Tower Osaka など）のプロモーションCG・映像から3D-MAP、シミュレーター、タッチパネル展示用インタラクティブコンテンツまで、幅広く制作。
2004	DVD（実写＋CG Short movie）-「まぼろしの色彩を追って～天平のバザラに会いたい」Recapturing the Lost Colors of BASARA 第8回2004 JPPAアウォード エディティング技術シルバー賞 the 2006 Newport Beach Film Festival入賞
2006	展示（立体視CG Short movie）-「Venus Venus」Siggraph2007 Computer Animation Festival 入賞
2006	DVD・展示 - (CG Short movie) - M.C.Escher「CONTRAST」Siggraph2007 Computer Animation Festival 入賞 The 11th Seoul International Cartoon & Animation Festival 入賞 California International Animation Festival 入賞
2007	展示 -「PLAN LIBRE/ル・コルビュジエ 4つの白い住宅 - 絵画＋時間＝建築」
2007	DVD・展示（CG Short movie）- Odilon Redon「NOIR」
2007	展示 -「犬山城」2007 Quest3D Demo Competitionグランプリ（sponsored by ACE-3D of the Netherlands）
2007	Web -「MUSEUM OF BEAUTY」(©Konica Minolta Holdings, Inc.) with collaboration from: CNN, STYLIST inc., Business Architects

Inc. Another Bookmark；SITE OF THE MONTH http://www.anotherbookmark.com/

008　權奇晶　KEE. J. CUON

2005	PSA Animation project - MTV KOREA「Do the right thing」
2005	入賞 -「Do the right thing」The ASIA APOLO AWARDS BEST PSA FINALIST / SINGAPORE
2006	上映 -「Do the right thing」ANNECY ANIMATION FESTIVAL OFFICIAL SELECTION / FRANCE
2005	Total Package - SPACE SHOWER TV「SS SPECIAL」
2005	Total Package - SPACE SHOWER TV「SPACE SHOWER THEATER」
2006	Motion Logo - SINGHA
2007	Exhibition Image - EPSON「Promotion DEMO image for EPSON OLED Display system」
2007	Channel Identity - ANIMAX

009　ダシ　DASI

1997	受賞 - アニメーション作品「独身者の機械」イメージフォーラムフェスティバル審査員特別賞 UP LINKよりビデオリリース
2001	受賞 - アニメーション作品「玉蟲少年」日本映画テレビ技術協会映像技術奨励賞 東京、大阪、京都ロードショー
2002	TV - NHK朝の連続テレビ小説「さくら」タイトル
2003	MV - Little Tempo「Musical Brain Food」(SPEEDSTAR)
2003	TV - 日本テレビ「Cooool TV」
2004	TV - NHK「天才てれびくんスペシャル ソフィア号の冒険」アニメーション
2006	CM - 明治製菓「Sweet Life」
2007	WEB - JTB「タビビト」

映像作家100人 2008
ワークプロファイル

015 ユーフラテス　EUPHRATES

～2005 TV - NHK教育番組「ピタゴラスイッチ」で「ピタ
ゴラ装置」「フレーミー」「10本アニメ」「○と△の
しゅうだん」他

2006 Introduction Movie - DNP - 「イデアの工場」
（佐藤雅彦＋ユーフラテス＋石川将也）New York
ADC 86th Annual Award Merit受賞

2006 Animation - 「TOKYO STRUT」（イメージフォー
ラム「TOKYO LOOP」）（佐藤雅彦＋うえ田みお）

2007 MV- 真心ブラザーズ「All I want to say to you」
（キューンレコード）

2007 MV- 真心ブラザーズ - 「きみとぼく」
（キューンレコード）

2007 MV- 栗コーダーカルテット - 「おじいさんの11ヶ
月」（ジェネオンエンタテインメント）

2007 Short Movie - イッセイミヤケ「A-POC INSIDE.」
（佐藤雅彦＋ユーフラテス）New York ADC 86th
Annual Award金賞受賞

2007 平成19年度文化庁メディア芸術祭アート部門優秀
賞受賞

016 後藤章治　SHOJI GOTO

2006 MV - OOIOO「UMO」
2006 上映 - RESFEST
2007 上映 - プラットフォーム国際アニメーションフェ
スティバル
2007 上映 - パリ環境映画祭
2007 上映 - シッチェス・カタロニア国際映画祭2007
受賞 - オタワ国際アニメーションフェスティバル
Best Music Video 賞
2008 上映 - ロッテルダム映画祭
2008 上映 - タンペレ国際短編映画祭
2008 上映 - エコシネマ・ギリシャ環境映画祭

017 グルーヴィジョンズ　GROOVISIONS

1997 MV - Pizzicato Five「lesson 3003」
（Nippon Columbia）

1997 MV - chappie「水中メガネ」
（Sony Music Entertainment）

2002 Artwork - 「NIKE PRESTO GRV1756」
music by Yukihiro Fukutomi（NIKE/Neverstop）

2002 Artwork - GAS DVD「GRV1778」music by
Yukihiro Fukutomi（DesignEXchange）

2004 Artwork - SOUND × VISIONS
「WATARIDORI GRV2153」
music by CORNELIUS（DesignEXchange）

2005 Artwork - 「GRV2156（Station navi）（EXPO
2005 AICHI JAPAN 愛・地球博エキスポビジョン）

2005 MV - HALFBY「RODEO MACHINE」
（SECOND ROYAL RECORDS）

2005 SPACE SHOWER Music Video Awards 06 BEST
CG/ANIMATION VIDEO 受賞

2006 MV - RIP SLYME「GOOD JOB!」
（Warner Music Japan）

2005-06 CM - ALL IN ONE（西日本シティ銀行）

2006 MV - HALFBY「SCREW THE PLAN」
（TOY'S FACTORY Inc.）
RESFEST 2006 Japan Tour
/ Audience Choice Award Best Music Video 受賞

2007 MV - RIP SLYME「SPEED KING」
（Warner Music Japan）

018 芳賀薫　KAORU HAGA

2001 受賞 - 「NISSAN CUBE」ニューヨークフィルム
フェスティバル ブロンズ受賞、ACC賞受賞

2005 受賞 - 「ラチェット & クランク3」ACC CMフェス
ティバルシルバー受賞

2006 受賞 - SPACE SHOWER TV MUSIC VIDEO AWARDS
'06 奥田民生「海の中へ」MALE VIDEO WINNER
平井堅「POP STAR」POP VIDEO WINNER

2006 受賞 - 47th CLIO AWARDS
奥田民生「海の中へ」MV Shortlist

映像作家100人 2008
ワークプロファイル

2007 受賞 - 48th CLIO AWARDS 日清食品「Freedom Project」Integrated Campaign Shortlist

019 半崎信朗 TOSHIAKI HANZAKI

2005 Original Work -「Birds（鳥の街）」DigiCon6＋1最優秀賞
2006 CM -「ユナイテッド・シネマ 劇場マナーCM」
2007 Opening Title - 劇団「田村亮一座」
2007 Animation＋SE -「Sony Talk」
2007 Animation＋SE -「NISSAN global website」
2007 Original Work -「Birthday」
2008 Title Movie - TBSドラマ「エジソンの母」

020 針谷建二郎 KENJIRO HARIGAI

2005 MV - Chisako Mikami「相対形」（UNIVERSAL MUSIC K.K.,）」
2006 MV - Chara「世界」（UNIVERSAL MUSIC K.K.,）
2006 MV - m-flo loves BONNIE PINK「Love Song」（rhythmzone）
2007 MV - 椎名林檎＋斉藤ネコ「茎」（TOSHIBA EMI）
2007 MV - FREE TEMPO「Dreaming」（SONY MUSIC PLAYERS）
2007 Short Movie -「BURTON ak Project」（BURTON）

021 長谷川踏太 TOTA HASEGAWA

2001 CI - Sony connected identity（Sony）
2001 CI - テレビ朝日（テレビ朝日）
2001 Instalation - You me who at KDDI Design Studio
2003〜 雑誌連載 -「モノサシに目印」（毎日コミュニケーションズ）
2006 Design - Seiko Spectrum Watch
2006 Interface Design -「P703i」（Panasonic）
2007 Design - Tezuka x Uniqlo T-shirts
2007 ウィンドウディスプレー - Aspesi Shop（ASPES）

022 橋本ダイスケ DAISUKE HASHIMOTO

2001 入賞 - JAPAN DIGITALANIMATION FESTIVAL「面接官」
2001 受賞 - UNITED CINEMA ANIMATION FESTIVAL「面接官」審査員特別賞
2004 入賞 - Promax&BDA LaLaTV「イメージ篇」
2005 受賞 - 平成17年度（第9回）文化庁メディア芸術祭 アニメーション部門「flowery」優秀賞
2006 入賞 - annecy2006 Movie Plus「ジャングル篇」&「flowery」
2006 受賞 - Promax WORLD GOLD AWARDS 2006 FUNNIEST PROMOTION部門 WOWOW映画宣伝「プロレス篇」銀賞
2006 入賞 - OTTAWA INTERNATIONAL ANIMATION FESTIVAL Movie Plus Station-ID「ラインアニメ篇」
2008 招待 - The First Children International Film Festival in Bangkok「flowery」

023 ハートボム HEART BOMB

2006 MV - endive「Liberty planet」（ビクターエンターテイメント）
2006 映像インスタレーション -「PLAN.E.T」（iseneehihinee）
2006 DVD -「Screen Savers」MUSTONE「妖怪展」（NANZUKA UNDERGROUND）
2006 VJ -「All night FUJI」FUJI ROCK FESTIVAL '06（Third culture）
2007 VJ -「CONNECT07」両国国技館（ハイネケン、ブランニューメイド、宇宙警備隊）
2007 MV - 詩人三代目魚武濱田成夫「あいしてる」他7本制作（東芝EMI）
2007 MV - 大沢伸一「Last Days」（エイベックス, チーム☆ラボ、鈴木庸平）
2007 MV - Wrench「feel more」（Cutting Edge、Third culture）

映像作家100人 2008
ワークプロファイル

033 ジュウリョク　JURYOKU

2004 入選 -「The poetry of suburbs」RESFEST2005 ワールドツアー

2005 Original Work -「fit-ment」graf、Yoshio Kubo とのコラボレーションによる作品

2006 作品制作 -「motion texture DVD」

2007 作品制作 - アートブック「wow10」

034 ケープラスミー　K＋ME

2004 Short Movie - La Kaltso

2005 個展 - Man Standing Up

2007 Animation - Hadagine

2007 MV - Screaming Dance

2008 個展 - Weirdos

035 喜田夏記　NATSUKI KIDA

2004 招待 - onedotzero08　MV「駅ニテ」

2004 招待 - エジンバラ国際映画祭　MV「駅ニテ」

2004 招待 - RESFEST Japan Tour-Resmix Electronica - MV「カゲロウ」

2005 招待 - Vila do Conde（ポルトガル映画祭） - Japan Lounge

2005 出展 - SICAF（韓国国際アニメーションフェスティバル）MV「カゲロウ」

2006 出展 - Anifest MV「駅ニテ」「カゲロウ」- チェコ

2006 出展 - エジンバラ国際映画祭 MV「velmouth flowers」

2006 出展 - RESFEST Japan Tour-Resmix Electronica - MV「cherry the dustman」作品招待

2006 招待 - 文化庁メディア芸術祭「資生堂MAJOLICA MAJORCA web movie chapter 10」エンターテイメント部門 審査員推薦作品

2007 上映 - ロンドン/ヴィクトリア＆アルバート美術館 企画展

036 キム・スンヨン　KIM SEUNG YONG

2001 Documentary -「チベットチベット 2002 招待 - 台湾国際ドキュメンタリー映画祭正式招待 オープニング

2004 上映 - 東京平和映画祭 クロージング

2005 招待 - 山形国際ドキュメンタリー映画祭

2006 受賞 - オレゴンユージン映画祭、観客賞

2007 Documentary -「雲南ＣＯＬＯＲＦＲＥＥ」

2008 リリースパーティ - 六本木スーパーデラックス他

2008 上映 - 大阪民族学博物館みんぱく

037 木村敏子　TOSHIKO KIMURA

2002 個展 - ROCKET - 原宿

2005 MV - Capitol K「NOMAD JUNK」

2005 個展 - LAPNET SHIP

2006 アートワーク提供 - And-A

2006 MV - SOUTH「Up Close and Personal」

2007 Short Movie - NHK POPJAM W＋K監修番組「東京.NOW」

2008 Product Design - NEC（Toshiko Kimura Model）

038 北山大介　DAISUKE KITAYAMA

2000-08　TV - J SPORTS「WORLD SOCCER NEWS FOOT!」

2001 MV - CORNELIUS「Point of View Point」

2002 MV - カジヒデキ「Footballing Weekenders」

2002 MV - TAHITI 80「Wallpaper For The Soul」

2005 MV - HARCO「NIGHT HIKE」

2005 MV - アナ「血湧き肉踊る」

2007 MV - アナ「FLASH」

2008 MV - bonobos「Someway」

映像作家100人 2008
ワークプロファイル

Ball」ニューヨークフェスティバル ファイナリスト

2006	受賞 - トヨタ自動車 ist「DJ」「ライティング」ニューヨークフェスティバル ファイナリスト
2007	受賞 - 第44回ギャラクシー賞 IGNIO「best of sports～Autumn」奨励賞受賞
2007	受賞 - SPACE SHOWER TV MUSIC VIDEO AWARDS '07
2007	受賞 - BEAT CRUSADERS「TONIGHT, TONIGHT, TONIGHT」MV BEST ROCK VIDEO
2007	受賞 - SPACE SHOWER MUSIC VIDEO AWARDS '07
2007	受賞 - YOUR SONG IS GOOD「SUPER SOUL MEETIN'」MV CONCEPT VIDEO WINNER

044　小嶋貴之　TAKAYUKI KOJIMA

1998	入賞 - VIBE STATION ID コンテストにてファイナリスト
2000	入賞 - FEED「Yellow」IMN-TV（アメリカケーブルTV）にトップ10選出
2002	入賞 - 田中雄一郎「サソリの詩」（ポリスター）RESFEST2002 ワールドツアー
2003	入賞 - downy「形而上学」（ポリスター）RESFEST2003 Japan Tour
2005	MV - Her space holiday「Forever and a day」（&records）スペーシャワー VMC視聴者投票企画「edge」1位
2008	入賞 - LITE「tomorrow」（UK プロジェクト）SPACE SHOWER TV MUSIC VIDEO AWARDS '08 ART DIRECTION部門

045　黒田賢　SATOSHI KURODA

2005	Original Work -「あるひとつの方向性」平成17年度（第9回）文化庁メディア芸術祭アニメーション部門／短編にて審査員推薦作品
2006	Original Work -「あるひとつの方向性」RESFEST 2006 World Tourにて招待上映
2006	CM - ライオン デンターシステマ「遊泳物体EX」篇

（Director＋CG）

2007	MV - GREAT ADVENTURE「THE AUDIENCE」（Director＋CG）
2006	Web Movie - HONDA NO SAME WAY project「CR250R」（Director＋CG）
2007	MV - WAGDUG FUTURISTIC UNITY「ILL MACHINE（×ULTRA BRAiN）」（Director＋CG）
2008	MV - L-VOKAL「万歳」（Director＋CG）
2008	VP - Panasonic Luminax Fx500「フリースタイルスポーツ篇」（Director＋CG）

046　くろやなぎてっぺい　TEPPEI KUROYANAGI

2007	MV - ストレイテナー「ALIBI」（EMI MUSIC JAPAN）
2007	MV - 椎名林檎＆齋藤ネコ「浴室」（EMI MUSIC JAPAN）
2007	Title Package - NHKスペシャル「ビューティー☆ウォーズ」
2007	TV Animation -「ビン子の秘伝カリー」（テレビ東京）
2007	CM - 文化庁メディア芸術祭「徳島展篇」
2008	GAME - SPACE INVADERS EXTREME アートディレクション
2008	TV - SMAP×SMAPブリッジ映像制作

047　牧鉄兵　TEPPEI MAKI

2007	MV - 沢瀉「kokiriko bushi」
2007	MV - DJ Kentaro「Tasogare High way High」
2007	TV -「ZAMURAI TV 弐」参加
2008	MV - Momoi Halko「Sunday early moning」

048　メタファー　METAPHOR

| 2007 | Web -「京都造形芸術大学」 |
| 2007 | 出展 - water展（21_21 DESIGN SIGHT 第2回企画展） |

映像作家100人 2008
ワークプロファイル

映像作家100人 2008
ワークプロファイル

| 2007 | 出展 - CUBE installation
（METAMORPHOSE2007） |
| 2008 | Web - 「DJ LAW SKOOL」
http://www.djlawskool.com |

066　大原大次郎　DAIJIRO OHARA

2003	OP - ピエール瀧「究極ホ乳類ニシイ」（Ki/oon Records）
2004	TV - 「電気グルーヴ Special」（SPACE SHOWER TV）
2005	TV - ガレッジセール「プリティガレッジ」（日本テレビ）
2005	MV - ASA-CHANG&巡礼「ライブのジュンレイ」 （Ki/oon Records）
2006	TV - 「FREAK OUT!」（cool sound、SPACE SHOWER TV）
2007	DVD「ぐうぜんのきろく2」オープニングアニメー ション制作（カクバリズム）
2007	MV - POLYSICS「コンピューターおばあちゃん」 （Ki/oon Records）
2008	MV - キセル「ビューティフルデイ」（カクバリズム）

068　大橋陽　YO OHASHI

| 2007 | DVD - 木村カエラ「LIVE Scratch~上がってますっ
てばTOUR@武道館」
（©Columbia Music Entertainment） |
| 2007 | DVD - Every Little Thing「Every Little Thing
10th Anniversary Special Live at Nippon
Budokan」（©AVEX ENTERTAINMENT） |

067　岡田尚志　TAKASHI OKADA

| 2006 | 受賞 - 「what-scary-strange-amazing-
complexity」adbe Motion Award animation部
門 優勝 |
| 2007 | 入選 - 「trffdg」第11回文化庁メディア芸術祭 審査
委員会推薦作品 アート部門 |

068　オンナコドモ　ONNACODOMO

2007	DVD - 「The World of onnacodomo」
2007	個展 - 「onnacodomo展」吉祥寺にじ画廊
2007	展示 - 「CALM Tree featuring Kazuaki Takeda X onnacodomo」青山Rocket

069　大月壮　SOU OOTSUKI

2005	DVD - 「Comedy News Show DVD1.2」（© CLUBKING）
2005	DVD - 「バナナマンのシャブりなコメディ/もっと燃 えろ」（©CLUBKING）
2005	MV&DVD - 「Fuuri」（©NOS inc, 2005）
2006	CM - 「No Music No Life」（©Tower Record）
2006	TV Title - 「NHK World Soccer」（©NHK情報ネット ワーク）
2007	TV - 「ZAMURAI TV弐 - 鎮座DOPENESS remix」（© SPACE SHOWER TV）
2007	MV - APOGEE - 「Just a seeker' s song」（©Victor Entertainment, Inc.）

070　OTAS

2006	Promo - 「ABC OSCARS 07」（SG//ARTS）
2007	Main Title - 「PROJECT RUNWAY」（SG// ARTS）
2007	Main Title - 「AMERICA' S NEXT PRODUCER」 （SG//ARTS）
2007	Main Title - 「LAST COMIC STANDING」（SG// ARTS）
2007	Promo - 「ABC DANCE WAR」（SG//ARTS）
2007	Main Title - 「TOP CHEF」（SG//ARTS）
2008	Main Title - 「STEP IT UP」（SG//ARTS）

映像作家100人 2008
ワークプロファイル

<table>
<tr><td>071</td><td colspan="2">パワーグラフィックス
POWER GRAPHIXX INC.</td></tr>
<tr><td>1999</td><td colspan="2">受賞 -Vibe Station IDコンテスト準グランプリ</td></tr>
<tr><td>2002</td><td colspan="2">MV -「Wingspan」「Dusseldorf Funk」
Cymbals（Victor Entertainment Inc.）</td></tr>
<tr><td>2003</td><td colspan="2">CM - NTV Station ID「GO! SHIODOME」</td></tr>
<tr><td>2005</td><td colspan="2">受賞 -「Roundscape」第8回文化庁メディア芸術
祭 アート部門審査員推薦作品</td></tr>
<tr><td>2005</td><td colspan="2">CM -「KYOCERA WX310K」</td></tr>
<tr><td>2005</td><td colspan="2">Opening Movie -「METAL GEAR AC!D 2」</td></tr>
</table>

072	榊原澄人	SUMITO SAKAKIBARA

2005	受賞 - 英国アニメックス学生アニメーションフェ スティバル 大賞
2005	受賞 - デジタルアートアワード 大賞
2005	受賞 - ロイヤルテレヴィジョンソサエティー学生 アニメーション英国全国大会 一位
2005	受賞 - メディア芸術祭:短編アニメーション部門 審 査員賞
2005	受賞 - 英国王立芸術大学院・パッションプライズ一位
2006	受賞 - 平成17年度文化庁メディア芸術祭アニメー ション部門 大賞
2006	受賞 - 英国アカデミー賞短編アニメーション部門 ノミネート
2006	受賞 -国際漫画・アニメフェスティバル グランプリ

073	笹生宗慶	MUNECHIKA SASAO

2007	CG - SMAP×SMAPブリッジ映像、BABY SMAP テーマ「昔、流行ったいいモノ」
2007	CG - 土曜ドラマ「ライアーゲーム」CX
2007	OP - 湘南の風「風伝説」DVD
2007	LED - SMAP×SMAP特別編「いま いじめてる君 へ...」CX OP LED映像
2007	VFX - 土曜ドラマ「フライトパニック」CX
2007	CG -「ウゴウゴルーガ/復活!!じゃないよ!?スペ シャル」ヴァーチャルセットデザイン

2008	LIVE -「忌野清志郎 完全復活祭武道館」オープニン グ映像他
2008	MV - TRAKS BOYS「starburst」

074	関根光才	KOSAI SEKINE

2005	受賞 - ニューヨーク短編映画祭 最優秀外国映画賞
2005	Short Film -「RIGHT PLACE」
2006	受賞 - ニューヨークフェスティバル ゴールド・他
2006	受賞 - カンヌ国際広告祭 ヤングディレクターズ・ アワード グランプリ他
2006	CM - 福岡市人権尊重週間「黒板篇」
2006	CM - レインダンス映画祭＋DIESEL「Daughter篇」
2007	Webムービー - NEC Theatre#3「Find Your Gift篇」
2007	入選 - AdFest ベストディレクター

075	柴田大輔	DAISUKE SHIBATA

2002	受賞 - NOVA NOVAうさぎ「デビュー」「散歩」 ACC CMフェスティバル ACCファイナリスト
2003	受賞 - ShortFilm「License」SantaFe Film Festivalグランプリ
2004	受賞 - ShortFilm「P.O.W」Clermont Ferrand Film Festivalノミネート その他10カ国ノミネート
2005	受賞 - ダイドードリンコ「ELECTRIC」アジアパシ フィック広告祭 ブロンズ賞
2005	受賞 - ASIAN KUNG-FU GENERATION「君の 街まで」SPACE SHOWER TV MUSIC VIDEO AWARDS ベストコンセプト賞
2005	受賞 - マルマン 禁煙パイポ「HOSPITAL」 「MEETING ROOM」ACC CM フェスティバル ブ ロンズ受賞
2007	受賞 - リクルート B-ing 06 ショッカーシリーズ ACC CMフェスティバル シルバー受賞
2007	受賞 - 万有製薬 ロングヘアカンフーマン Gyao Creative Award 2007 グランプリ

Art Center College Library
1700 Lida St.
Pasadena, CA 91103

映像作家１００人 ２００８
ワークプロファイル

2006	TV - 真鍋かをり司会の「ブログの女王」（テレビ東京）オープニング映像、キャラクター制作
2007	BOOK -「みんなのトニオちゃんリターンズ」単行本発売
2008	DVD - ポニーキャニオンよりDVD作品集発売予定

083　須藤カンジ　KANJI SUTO

2005	CM - Victor new LipLap CM （Miz玉篇）
2006	MV - CHEMISTRY「遠影」（Defstar Records）
2006	MV - GODIEGO「MONKEY MAGIC 2006」（Universal Music）
2006	MV - SEAMO「ルパン ザ ファイヤー」（BMGジャパン）
2007	受賞 - SPACE SHOWER TV MUSIC VIDEO AWARDS '07 BEST ART DIRECTION RADWIMPS「有神論」
2007	MV - The Birthday「アリシア」（Universal Music）
2007	MV - 矢井田瞳「I Love You の 形」（青空レコード）

084　高木正勝　TAKAGI MASAKATSU

2002	個展 -「world is so beautiful」アニエスb.全国９店舗にて展示
2002	TV - NHK「美と出会う」オープニング映像＋音楽制作
2003~04	映像演出 - デヴィッド・シルヴィアンのワールドツアー（７カ国１７都市）
2004	ダンス作品 -「Wonder Girl」映像＋音楽制作 - 青山スパイラルホール/東京
2004	MV - UA「Lightning」
2006	ビジュアルブック＋DVD -「Bloomy Girls」（Bluemark＋Epiphany Works）- 東京
2006	コンサート -「Private/ Public」開催 - ラフォーレ原宿/東京
2007	CM -「Audi TT」オーストラリアAudi社のためのイメージビデオ制作＋コンサート（ミュージアム・オブ・コンテンポラリー・アート・シドニー）

085　タナカカツキ　KATSUKI TANAKA

2007	展示 -「タナカカツキのマトリョニメ展」（ギャラリー sak?）
2007	展示 -「タナカカツキの顔ハメ☆パノラーーーマ！展」（オリンパス）
2007	展示 -「タナカカツキの太郎ビーム！展」（岡本太郎記念館）
2007	展示 - 文化庁メディア芸術祭「日本の表現力」展示映像「イエス☆パノラーマ！360°」

086　田中賢一郎　KENICHIRO TANAKA

2000	受賞 - アジア・パシフィック広告祭VFX部門シルバー賞
2001	受賞 - Siggraph 2001 ElectronicTheater
2001〜2003	CM - ソラリアプラザ企業イメージ「ワンダフルワールド篇」「アリダンス篇」「羊ダンス篇」「マイウェイ！篇」ほか
2002	CM - sony WEGA「唄う狼篇」
2003	CM -「フンドーキン／ライオンとうさぎ篇」
2003	CM - ダスキン「人形篇」
2004	番組オープニング - アテネオリンピック民放共通オープニング
2006〜	CGI - 映画「蟲師」「ゲゲゲの鬼太郎」「監督バンザイ」

087　田中裕介　YUSUKE TANAKA

2005	受賞 -MTV Video Music Award 特殊映像技術賞「イルカ」SOUL'd OUT
2006	受賞 - NY ADC 銅賞「Water for life」
2006	受賞 - Promax&BDA銀賞 SPACE SHOWER TV「TUCKER ID」
2006	MV -「バイマイメロディー」平井堅
2006	受賞 - MTV Video Music Award 特殊映像技術賞「ゴースト・ソング」APOGEE
2007	受賞 - D&AD年鑑掲載「ツナガルキモチ」Missing Link
2007	SPACE SHOWER TV MUSIC VIDEO

AWARDS '07 BEST DIRECTOR

2008 CM - Vidal Sasoon Collaboration Video 「ROCK STEADY」安室奈美恵

タムデム　TAMDEM

2007 MV - KAN TAKAGI 「T.I.M.E」feat. ANI・BOSE (スチャダラパー)、VERBAL (m-flo) and LUPE FIASCO 「G-SHOCK 25th Anniversary ORIGINAL TRACK」

2007 TV - SPACE SHOWER TV 「ZAMURAI TV」HIFANA feat. IZUPON

2007 Opening Title - ANIMAX 「年末年始がおもしろい1週間」

2007 VJ - TOWA TEI 「MOTIVATION」

2007 VJ - KENTARO TAKIZAWA 「HEART TO HEART」RELEASE PARTY

2007 LIVE - YUKI LIVE "5-star" 「HEY! YOU!」

2007 VJ - Roen×DIET BUTCHER SLIM SKIN「HAZE」

TANGE FILMS

2006 受賞 - 「TCM Award 2006」審査員特別賞、Flux賞

2007 Short Movie - 「Your Sound」

2007 Illustraion - 「New Beetle」

2007 Short Movie - 「AKARUI MUSYOKU」

2007 MV - sanrio 「chu chu chu」

2007 Characror Design - 「取手KEIRIN」

2008 Opening Movie - 「Brillia Shortshorts Theater」

谷篤　ATSUSHI TANI

2003 MV- KEN ISHII 「Strobe Enhanced」(now on media)

2004 MV - NIRGILIS 「KING」(chukuri record)

2005 SPOT - MTV 「気がきいている君篇」

2006 MV - BENNIE K 「DISCO先輩」(FOR LIFE MUSIC ENTERTAINMENT)

2006 CM - NTT DoCoMo 「iD 『登場篇』」

2006 MV - SMAP 「ありがとう」(Victor Entertainment)

2007 CM - ファミリーマート 「Welcom T-POINT 『Block篇/City篇/Card篇』」

2008 MV - キリンジ 「朝焼けは雨のきざし」(Columbia Music Entertainment)

丹治まさみ　MASAMI TANJI

1998 受賞 - 「Wavy Award '98」3Dグラフィック＆アニメーション賞

2002 Original Animation - 「TOWER OF BEBEL」

2003 CG監督 - 劇場アニメーション 「茄子 アンダルシアの夏」

2004 Original Animation - 「blidge」、DVD 「PIX Vol.2」に収録

2004 書籍 - 「デジタル映像制作ガイドブック」(ワークスコーポレーション)

2005 MV - 戸田誠司 「Memory」(ナウオンメディア)

2005 CG - 安室奈美恵 「WoWa」MV (エイベックス・トラックス)

2007 CG - DVDアニメーション 「茄子 スーツケースの渡り鳥」

田尾創樹　SOJU TAO

2006 MV - Perfectdancer feart. Tazumayama 「Thank you」(OkamePro)

2006 MV - Kuchibilu 「Out of Controal」(OkamePro)

2006 MV - Okamehachimoku 「Shirasagi-kun」(OkamePro)

2007 MV - Perfectdancer 「Jada Hey Ho」(OkamePro)

2007 MV - Okamehachimoku 「Anoko no hitomi wa rasenjyou」(OkamePro)

2007 MV - Perfectdancer 「Shigemitsu」(OkamePro)

映像作家１００人 ２００８
ワークプロファイル

093　辻川幸一郎　KOICHIRO TSUJIKAWA

2007	展覧会 - 「大声展 Get It Louder 2007」 - 広州/上海/北京
2007	受賞 - 「第一回インビテーション・アワード」Music（WARNER MUSIC JAPAN）
2007	受賞 - 「平成18年度（第10回）文化庁メディア芸術祭」Fit Song（WARNER MUSIC JAPAN）
2007-2008	展覧会 - 「六本木クロッシング 2007：未来への脈動」展 - 森美術館
2008	受賞 - 「デジタル・コンテンツ・オブ・ジ・イヤー'07/第13回ＡＭＤアワード」きまぐれロボット（NTTドコモ、角川モバイル、角川ザ・テレビジョン、アスミック・エース エンタテインメント）

094　上田大樹　TAIKI UEDA

2000	受賞 - 「ぴあフィルムフェスティバル」準グランプリ
2003	受賞 - 「ぴあフィルムフェスティバル」グランプリ
2003	TV - 「HR」タイトル映像（フジテレビジョン）
2004	TV - 「いないいないばあっ！」タイトル映像（NHK）
2005	MV - 木村カエラ「リルラリルハ」（Columbia Music Entertainment）
2005	Animation - CHANEL銀座ビル ファサードアニメーション（CHANEL）
2006	LIVE - レミオロメン tour「program」演出映像（Oolom-sha Co Ltd.,）
2007	LIVE演出映像 - Mr.Children "HOME" tour「シーソーゲーム」（Oolom-sha Co Ltd.）

095　宇川直宏　UKAWA NAOHIRO

1976	Exhibition - 「ビッコロモビルスーツ」（小４）香川県夏休みエコ絵画コンクール法務大臣賞受賞

096　ワウラブ　WOWLAB

2006	Installation - 「Motion Texture」- せんだいメディアテーク
2007	Installation - 「Tengible」- TENT LONDON
2007	Installation - 「Light Rain」- Seoul Design Festival

097　耶雲哉治　SAIJI YAKUMO

2003	映画オープニング映像 - 「踊る大捜査線 THE MOVIE 2」
2003	CM - 読売新聞「文芸小説PR」
2004	グラビアDVD - スーパー DVDカップ「磯山さやか風味」
2005	CM - モスバーガー「KATSUO」「パオチキン」
2006	ドキュメンタリー DVD - 「上村愛子に起こった30日間のほぼすべて」
2007	CM - ALSOK「ピンチにはやい！」
2007	CM - キリンビール「麒麟淡麗〈生〉」
2007	CM - オリンピック招致委員会「みのさん語る」「有森さん語る」「野口さん語る」

098　山口崇司　TAKASHI YAMAGUCHI

2001	入選 - Siggraph2001 Electronic Theater
2001	入選 - 平成13年度 第5回 文化庁メディア芸術祭 審査員推薦作品
2002	Mobileアプリ - 「LEDJAVa」「punk_lock（The END 2003年度TDCインタラクティブデザイン賞）
2005	出展 - 「D-Day」パリ・ポンピドーセンター
2007	展示 - プラネタリウム MEGASTAR-II cosmos「偶然の惑星」偶然の映像（日本科学未来館）
2007	DVD - d.v.d ファーストDVD＋CD「01>01」リリース（HEADZ）
2007	出展 - 「六本木クロッシング 2007：未来への脈動」展 - 森美術館
2008	Live - transmediale.08 - ベルリン

映像作家
100人
2008

JAPANESE
MOTION GRAPHIC
CREATORS 2008

2008 年 4 月 25 日 初版第一刷発行

編集　庄野祐輔 古屋蔵人 藤田夏海

編集協力　服部全宏 yoyo. 林永子 山口浩司

協力　山本加奈

表紙デザイン　前田晃伸

本文デザイン　庄野祐輔 古屋蔵人

挿絵（P004-009）河野未彩

撮影（P012-P031）森川智之

翻訳　ジェレミー・ハーレイ 藤田夏海

制作進行　石井早耶香

発行人　籔内康一

発売　株式会社ビー・エヌ・エヌ新社

〒 104-0042
東京都中央区入船 3-7-2 35 山京ビル
FAX. 03-5543-3108

印刷　株式会社シナノ

※本書の一部または全部について、著作権上㈱ビー・エヌ・エヌ新社
　および著作権者の承諾を得ずに無断で複写、複製することは禁じら
　れております。
※本書について、電話でのお問い合わせには一切応じられません。
※乱丁本・落丁本はお取り替えいたします。FAXにてご連絡下さい。
※定価はカバーに記載してあります。

Copyright © 2008 by BNN, Inc.

Printed in Japan

ISBN 978-4-86100-576-3

Art Center College of Design
Library
1700 Lida Street
Pasadena, Calif. 91103

11 March '09   IAI   49.50   (55.00)   409604